Survival for the Fittest: the Australian Institute of Sport official cookbook for busy athletes has been produced in association with Nestlé Australia Ltd. ABN 77 000 011 316

First published in 1999
Reprinted in 2000
Murdoch Magazines Pty Ltd (Custom Books division)
Pier 8/9 Hickson Road, Walsh Bay NSW
GPO Box 1203 Sydney NSW 1045
Telephone (02) 8220 2000
ABN 62 007 619 767

Manager, Custom Books:	Nicola Hartley
Design & Layout:	Amanda Adler, Murdoch Magazines (Creative Services division)
Consulting Editor:	Susin Chow
Food Stylist:	Patrick Collins
Food Stylist's Assistant:	Jane Collins

Special thanks to the following for their assistance in this publication: Orson & Blake, Woollahra; Empire Homewares, Darlinghurst; Portmans, Melbourne; Made in Japan, Paddington.

The authors would also like to thank Nathan Lewis for his valuable contribution to the book, and we are indebted to Susan Wright who made it happen, and happen quickly!

We thank the athletes who provided quotes for this book. Involvement in this project does not imply support of any commercial product or association with the AIS or Nestlé Australia Ltd.

Sports images supplied by the National Sport Information Centre, Australian Sports Commission. Selected sports images on pages 21, 69, 87, 109, courtesy Ansett Collection, Australian Sports Commission. Sports image on page 37, courtesy David Searle.

First edition printed by Websdale Printing Pty Ltd, NSW
Reprinted by australian book connection

Distributed by Allen & Unwin
9 Atchison Street, St Leonards NSW 2065 Australia

National Library of Australia Cataloguing-in-Publication Data

Survival for the Fittest: the Australian Institute of Sport official cookbook for busy athletes

ISBN 1 876652 06 3

1. Physical fitness — Nutritional aspects. 2. Athletes — Nutrition. 3. Quantity cookery. I. Burke, Louise. II. Australian Sports Commission. III. Australian Institute of Sport. IV. Title.

613.2

survival

FOR THE FITTEST

about this book

This book grew out of the cooking classes which we have been running with our athletes for 10 years. Although the AIS is at the cutting edge of the science of sports nutrition, this vault of knowlege can't be put into practice unless our athletes feel at home in the kitchen. They are often young and haven't had much time to develop their cooking skills. In the AIS residence dining hall, we can feed our athletes for the day, but we must also educate them to feed themselves for the future. We recognise that today's athletes are tired after training, have busy lives with many commitments, and desire tasty food that can be shared with others. In our cooking classes we focus on recipes that are quick, delicious, foolproof for non-elite chefs and packed with the nutritional value which athletes need.

To write *Survival for the Fittest*, we have talked to many AIS athletes and coaches, as well as other athletes with whom we have worked. Throughout this book, we have shared with you the tips and hints from these busy but motivated people.

This is more than a recipe book. It is the athlete's definitive guide to getting organised at home and cooking great meals, because performing well in the kitchen plays a key role in performing well in your sport.

contents

the winning diet ~ a recipe for success

Whether you are going for gold, or for the satisfaction of a Personal Best, you need to be in shape, well-fuelled and confident. Good eating is one of the keys to achieving these goals. While there is no single menu that is perfect for the special training and competition needs of all athletes, there are some common ingredients that make up a winning diet for all sports, and healthy eating for all of us.

eating to train

1. Maintain Food Variety and Enjoyment

Variety at meals and across meals helps us enjoy what we eat, and ensures we find our nutrient needs in a range of good food sources. Priority goes to nutrient-rich foods that best look after our bodies' needs and keep us healthy, but there is room for all foods, especially those that are fun to eat or enjoyed on social occasions. Although popular diet books have spread the myth that certain foods shouldn't be eaten together, the truth is that meals are *improved* by mixing and matching foods. Combine foods cleverly to enhance the nutritional value of the total meal, as well as to enjoy the different colours, flavours and textures.

> Fruits and vegetables brighten your plate or a recipe, can add texture and crunch, and are packed with health benefits. They are a good source of B-carotene and other families of protective phyto-chemicals. Vitamin C is another vitamin with antioxidant activity. Enrich your meals with tropical, citrus and berry fruits, or vegetables such as capsicum, tomatoes, broccoli, and herbs.

> Meet your daily target of 800-1200 mg of calcium with 3-4 serves of dairy or calcium-enriched soy products. Try milk or yogurt on cereal, reduced-fat cheese in a sandwich or on a homemade pizza, custard or yogurt for dessert, and a hot chocolate or fruit smoothie before bed.

> Pump iron into your diet with meals that include small but regular amounts of foods that contain well-absorbed iron such as red meats, shellfish and darker cuts of poultry. Other foods that are good sources of iron but are poorly absorbed include eggs, nuts, wholegrain cereals, beans and soy products, fortified breakfast cereals and green leafy vegetables. To boost iron availability mix and match these foods with those which are high in Vitamin C (e.g. fruit juice along with cereal at breakfast) or red/white meats (e.g. beans and lean mince in a chilli con carne).

2. Focus on Fuel Foods

The critical fuel for exercise is provided by the body's carbohydrate stores — a small amount of blood glucose and a larger amount of glycogen stored in muscle. Since these stores can only sustain a few hours of continuous exercise, they must be continually refilled from the carbohydrates in your diet. Running low on carbohydrates causes fatigue — you may have experienced how it feels to run out of fuel in a session — while chronic depletion may cause tiredness and ineffective training.

The body's carbohydrate needs increase the more you exert energy. For general health benefits and to fuel a light to moderate training program, carbohydrate foods should make up more than half of your total energy intake. Athletes in heavy daily training may need to achieve special carbohydrate intake targets. For maximum daily glycogen storage, you need an intake of 7–10 g carbohydrate per 1 kg body weight. For a typical endurance athlete, this means a daily intake of 400–700 g carbohydrate.

Nutritious, high-carbohydrate foods should be the first priority in your diet, but remember that sugar and sugary foods are compact and easy to eat, and therefore can be used to top up on fuel. If the time between training sessions is short (less than 8 hours), make every minute count towards muscle refuelling. If you can't eat a high-carbohydrate meal within 30–60 minutes of the work out, at least have a snack providing 50–100 g of carbohydrate to start the refuelling process.

> There are many nutritious carbohydrate-rich foods to enjoy, including grain foods such as bread, breakfast cereal, pasta, rice, noodles and couscous, the enormous variety of fruits, starchy vegetables (potato, sweet potato, corn) and legumes. Sweetened dairy products such as fruit dairy snacks, flavoured milk, custard and yogurt are also good fuel foods.

3. Go Light on Fats and Oils

Although our bodies need some fats and oils, our eating patterns usually exceed these requirements. The disadvantages of high-fat eating include an increased risk of health problems such as heart disease and some cancers, and of being overweight. For athletes, an added concern is that a high-fat intake displaces the energy we really need from carbohydrate foods. Watching your intake of fats and oils is good for all athletes, and makes room to eat more fuel foods, but, if you are also concerned with losing some body fat or keeping it off, it helps to pay special attention to low-fat eating strategies.

■ Reduce the size of the serve of meat in meals, and choose the lean cuts, removing any remaining fat or skin.

■ Choose low-fat and reduced-fat dairy products. Yogurt, milk, fruit dairy snacks and custard all come in great-tasting low-fat versions. Cheese can be found in reduced-fat and relatively low-fat forms, but you will still need to watch the amount you eat.

■ Use low-fat methods when preparing your meals. Cook with minimal amounts of added fat or oil – either dry-fry or stirfry in a small amount of oil or use spray-on oil, grill, roast on a rack, steam or microwave.

■ Don't smother your food in oil, butter, greasy sauces or dressings – spice up your food with sauces and relishes that are light and tasty instead. Try low-oil dressings, or herbs and lemon juice on salads. Replace butter and margarine on sandwiches with a spread of mustard, salsa, avocado or light mayonnaise.

■ Be aware of the hidden fat inside many baked or prepared food items, especially treats such as chocolate, rich desserts, cakes and biscuits. Enjoy these in small amounts, and go for quality rather than quantity.

■ Learn to read labels to identify the total fat content of food (see page 124).

4. Stay Cool with Fluids

Sweating is the body's way of getting rid of the heat generated by exercise, and sweating rates increase as the work becomes harder or the environment becomes hotter. Being in 'fluid balance' means replacing losses from day to day, but also preventing dehydration during each training session. You can't train your body to get used to being dehydrated, just like your car can't be trained to run with an empty radiator. Fluid needs will be important to your competition strategies, so start to develop good drinking habits in advance. Apart from the practice, you can look forward to better training when you are better hydrated. Be organised rather than haphazard in keeping up fluid intake, especially when it is hot or you have suddenly moved to a warmer climate. Always carry your own water bottle so that you can get a drink wherever you are.

Get a feel for your sweat losses during a work out, and how well you replace these. Weigh yourself (towelled down and in minimal clothing) before and after the session. Changes do not mean you have lost weight (fat) – they simply reflect dehydration. Each 1 kg of bodyweight 'lost' is equal to 1 litre of fluid. During each work out, try to keep fluid deficits to 1 kg or less by drinking as often as is practical during the session.

eating to compete

1. Fuel Up for Your Event

Sufficient muscle fuel can be stored for most events with 24 hours of tapered training or rest and high-carbohydrate eating. Carbohydrate loading is a more specialised version of this practice, and is used by endurance and ultra-endurance athletes who compete in events lasting 2 hours or longer. Although it has enjoyed a lot of hype and mystery, carbohydrate loading is really just an extended period of fuelling up. Three days of exercise taper and high carbohydrate intake will increase muscle glycogen levels above their normal concentrations. This extra fuel won't make the athlete go faster, but it will prolong the time that they can maintain their optimal race pace.

Marathon runners of the past used to include an extreme "depletion phase" before loading to enhance their muscle glycogen gains, but modern sports scientists no longer consider this necessary. In fact, trying to complete the last week of training while depleted can make you feel weak and psyched out. If your event will benefit from extra glycogen stores, stick to the three-day fuelling program.

2. Eat a High-carbohydrate Pre-event Meal

The pre-event meal provides a final opportunity to top up fuel and fluid levels. It must also balance the discomfort of getting hungry during the event, with the risk of stomach problems arising from mixing food intake with pre-event nerves or high-intensity exercise.

A high-carbohydrate, low-fat meal or snack is the perfect choice for a pre-event meal. Depending on the time of day, you might like to adapt one of the meals that is part of your everyday winning diet. It is best to eat large meals 3–4 hours before you compete, although a light snack can usually be eaten 1–2 hours before your warm-up. Liquid meal supplements are better tolerated than a solid meal, particularly if you're feeling nervous. Each athlete has their own routine, based on individual needs and likes, and fine-tuned through experience, so experiment in training to find a plan that works for you.

PRE-EVENT MEALS
■ Breakfast cereal + low-fat milk + fruit
■ Muffins or crumpets + jam or honey
■ Pancakes + syrup
■ Toast + baked beans or tinned spaghetti
■ Creamed rice (made with low-fat milk)
■ Rolls or sandwiches + banana filling
■ Fruit salad + low-fat fruit yogurt
■ Pasta with tomato or low-fat sauce
■ Baked potatoes + low-fat filling
■ Sports bars or cereal bars and sports drink
■ Fruit smoothie (fruit + low-fat milk + yogurt or ice cream)
■ Liquid meal supplement

3. Hydrate and Refuel During the Event

Most of us know that severe dehydration has a dramatic effect on exercise performance, but even small fluid losses reduce performance and increase your feeling of having to make an effort. These effects can be subtle, and you may not notice dehydration slowly eating away at your performance, but, long before the effects are obvious, your work output will drop and your skills and concentration will deteriorate. In an ideal world, an athlete would drink enough fluid to cover their sweat losses during their event, but, in the real world of sport, this is not usually possible. A realistic goal is to use all opportunities to drink what is practical and comfortable in your sport. At best, most athletes only replace 50 per cent of their fluid losses during the event, so there is plenty of room for improvement.

Fluid is not the only requirement during some sports events. Carbohydrate depletion can occur in prolonged events requiring several hours of high-intensity exercise. You might know the feeling as "hitting the wall" or "bonking". But you can also run out of fuel in shorter events or games, when a busy competition schedule prevents complete refuelling between sessions. Extra fuel can be provided by consuming carbohydrates during the event. This strategy has been shown to benefit performance in events lasting longer than 90 minutes, but recent research has shown that benefits might also occur in events of as little as an hour duration, so experiment to see if carbohydrate intake works for your sport and for you.

> Drinking sports drinks is a practical way to refuel and rehydrate during exercise. The special formula of fluid, carbohydrate and electrolytes was developed to taste good while exercising, promoting an increase in total fluid intake as its first advantage. The formula also provides efficient delivery of carbohydrate. Some people think that sports drinks are only useful to elite athletes, but the issue concerns nutritional needs rather than sporting talent. If you are involved in a sport in which you are sweating and depleting fuel stores, then a sports drink is a simple answer to meet your special needs. Good use of a sports drink will improve your endurance and performance, regardless of your level of competition. This represents good value for the money spent on the sports drink.

- Look for all opportunities for fluid intake in your sport, both formal breaks such as half-time or substitutions, and informal breaks such as stoppages in play. Make sure fluids are always on hand. If trainers are unable to take fluids to players, educate the player to come to the boundary or court side for a quick drink.

- Take extra care in continuous events such as marathons and cycling races where athletes literally drink on the run. Concerns include gastric discomfort, or the time lost by slowing down to grab and consume a drink. However, remember that this time can be made up by better performance resulting from better hydration. With practice and special drinking devices, an athlete can learn to drink without sacrificing their pace.

- Consider refuelling with a sports drink in events greater than an hour in duration. A carbohydrate intake of 30–60 g per hour is recommended, and provided by 400–1000 mL per hour of sports drink. Even if you don't need the extra carbohydrate, a sweet-tasting drink is likely to be consumed more than water.

4. Eat and Drink to Recover Quickly After Events

Most competition schedules call for rapid recovery between events. Refuelling and rehydrating should become a priority in your post-competition activities, but you may have to juggle this with other commitments. Competition venues may not always provide access to suitable foods and drinks, so it makes sense to bring your own supplies. Good planning will see you bouncing back.

When quick refuelling is important, schedule your next meal or a substantial snack (50–100 g carbohydrate) for within the hour after an event. There are many food choices to suit your appetite and the available catering facilities. Remember that you will continue to sweat and lose fluid during your recovery. In fact, you will need to drink one and a half times the amount of your post-event fluid deficit over the next hours to restore fully your fluid balance. For example, if you are 2 kg (2 litres) lighter at the end of the event, you will need to drink 3 litres to ensure full rehydration.

> **IDEAS FOR 50 g SERVES OF CARBOHYDRATE**
> - 800-1000 mL sports drink
> - 500 mL fruit juice or soft drink
> - 250-350 mL fruit smoothie or liquid meal supplement
> - 1 jam or honey sandwich (thick-sliced bread + lots of jam or honey)
> - 3 muesli bars or 2 cereal bars
> - 3 medium-large pieces of fruit (e.g. apple, orange, banana)
> - 2 cups breakfast cereal + skim milk
> - 2 x 200 g cartons low-fat fruit yogurt
> - 1 cup of thick vegetable soup + large bread roll
> - 2 cups of fruit salad + $^1/_2$ carton of low-fat fruit yogurt
> - 1 large bread roll + banana filling
> - 60 g jellybeans or lollies or 70-80 g chocolate

how the fit survive ~ the skills & challenges

Getting on top of the shopping and cooking is not hard, and the pay-offs of good eating are great. Here, we've listed some key strategies and tips.

Where Possible, Use Teamwork

■ If you share a house, call a team meeting to organise that tasks are shared. When time or money is scarce, it helps to pool resources.

■ Don't worry if conflicting timetables mean you only meet up a few times a week. Use your time together to plan and roster the tasks of shopping or cooking. Use lists to communicate what is needed.

■ Use your rest day to do shopping and cooking tasks that help other housemates. You will be pleased to enjoy the same assistance on your busy days.

Acquire New Skills

■ Gradually master new cooking skills. Use recipes in this book to learn a style of cooking (e.g. a risotto or a stirfry) then branch out on your own by changing a few ingredients. Practice makes perfect!

■ Look out for tips from other athletes or good cooks. Take information from a variety of sources, and adapt it to your own needs.

Plan Ahead and Manage Your Time Well

■ Start with a well-organised and clean kitchen. This makes cooking quick and easy.

■ Make a list of useful items for the freezer, fridge and pantry, and keep these in stock. Note when stocks are running low and need replacing, and take advantage of supermarket specials to grab multiples of these items.

■ Plan your meals for the week ahead and note the required ingredients. Make a shopping list from this and add your general food stock needs.

- Avoid supermarkets in peak hours. Shop late or early so that you save time.
- Avoid shopping when you are hungry or tired — the shopping list is likely to go out the window.
- Only buy goods that you can use within their use-by-dates. Choose good-quality products that have been appropriately stored.
- Plan your meals to take advantage of leftovers or batch cooking. For example, if you are having rice as an accompaniment one night, cook extra to make into fried rice on the following evening. Pasta sauces can be served on the next night as a potato filling.
- Use your rest day to cook ahead for the week. Cook up one or two dishes that can be refrigerated or frozen. It's great when you come home late and tired from training to find that the hard work has been done.
- Even if you are cooking a meal for just one or two people, cook the whole recipe to ensure there are left-overs. (Cook double quantities if you are feeding a few.) This may save you from cooking again the next night, but you can also freeze leftovers in single-size portions. These will thaw or reheat quickly so you can have a meal in minutes. Invest in a good set of clear plastic containers that you can label and stack in the freezer.
- Prepare as much of the meal as you can before training (e.g. make the pasta sauce or chop the ingredients for a stirfry) as this will speed up the cooking process when you get home.
- Plan snacks that can be eaten on the run or taken with you on your busy day — for example, single-serve cereals, cartons of yogurt, cereal bars, fruit and even some leftovers will travel.
- Make up a loaf of sandwiches when you have roast meat or deli meats on hand. Meat or cheese sandwiches freeze well, and can have salad added when thawed.

LIST FOR THE FREEZER
Skinless chicken, lean mince, lean beef, lamb or pork fillets, frozen vegetables, frozen vegetable medleys and stirfry mixes, bread, pizza bases, muffins, crumpets, filo pastry, grated reduced-fat cheese

---

LIST FOR THE FRIDGE
Fresh fruit and vegetables, juices, hokkien noodles, fresh lasagne sheets, fresh pasta, reduced-fat cheese, low-fat yogurt and custard, milk, eggs, margarine, sauces (chilli, plum, chutney, tomato paste), minced herbs (garlic, ginger, curry paste) and condiments (mustard, low-oil dressings and mayonnaise)

LIST FOR THE PANTRY
Pasta, rice, couscous, oats, breakfast cereal, canned spaghetti, canned legumes (kidney beans, baked beans, chickpeas), tomato soup, canned fruit in natural juice, tuna and salmon, long-life milk, light evaporated milk, bottled pasta sauces, soy sauce, fish sauce, vinegar, rice cakes, cereal bars, muesli bars, dried herbs and spices, baking goods (sugar, flour, cornflour, custard powder, essences, cocoa), pancake mix, spray-on oil

Using Creative Shortcuts
- Invest in a few good cooking tools or household items that save time and produce quality outcomes. A good wok, large nonstick frying pan, microwave, sharp knives, lasagne dish and pizza trays (and cutter) are all good purchases. A rice cooker may also be useful.
- Make use of nutritious time-saver products available in supermarkets. There are many which can make a good meal, or form a base for quickly cooking a meal (see list).
- It sometimes helps to buy meat already trimmed or diced for a stirfry, or frozen and fresh vegetable stirfry mixes. They can cost a little extra, but often the time you save in meal preparation is worth this expense.
- Soften vegetables such as potato, pumpkin and carrots that need to be chopped for a recipe by placing them for 1-2 minutes in the microwave to make them easier to cut.
- Leftover rice and pasta can be frozen. To reheat, microwave or pour boiling water over it and drain.
- If you haven't got time to cook rice or pasta with a meal, use couscous. It can be prepared in minutes.
- Fresh pasta cooks more quickly than dried varieties. Gnocchi cooks in a minute, while fresh lasagne sheets cut the baking time in half.
- If you are not adventurous with flavouring dishes, make use of prepared pasta and stirfry sauces and even fresh soups. These can be used as the flavouring base of a dish to which you add your own choice of meat and vegetables.
- Jars of minced herbs provide authentic flavour and save you having to chop or grate items such as garlic or ginger and waste the unused portions. Some fresh herbs, for example parsley or coriander, are worth buying and you can also freeze them in small portions for later use.
- Be versatile. Know which ingredients are vital for a recipe and which can easily be replaced. Exchange recipe items with what you have in your fridge or pantry or according to which foods are in season or 'on special' in the supermarket.
- Choose recipes that are complete meals for single-portion freezing. If the dish is self-contained with meat, vegetables and a carbohydrate choice, you will need no meal preparation other than reheating or you may even be able to eat it straight from the container.

NUTRITIOUS TIME-SAVING PRODUCTS
- Tomato-based pasta sauces
- Some stirfry and casserole sauces (check the label for the fat content)
- Fresh or frozen pizza bases
- Fresh pasta
- Frozen vegetables and stirfry mixes
- Most fresh or canned soups (check fat content)
- Canned beans, chickpeas and other legumes
- Canned tomatoes, corn
- Pizza and tomato paste
- Minced herbs
- Long-life milk
- Custards and rice puddings in cartons
- Pancake mixes
- Spray-on oils for cooking
- LEAN CUISINE meals

off the beaten track

Variety is the key to a winning diet, but some athletes need or want to restrict their food choices. The following section will provide tips for some of the most common dietary modifications practised by athletes.

Vegetarianism

The vegetarian recipes included in this book were not developed just for vegetarian athletes. We encourage all athletes to incorporate vegetarian meals and new foods into their eating repertoires. This is part of varied eating.

However, for some athletes, vegetarian eating is a total way of life, chosen for reasons of religion, culture or environmental concern. Vegetarianism is not simply a matter of avoiding meat or animal foods and it is more than a plate of steamed vegetables. Not only do these ideas fail to do justice to vegetarian eating, they can be a cause of poor performance. Balanced vegetarian eating means finding alternative food sources to supply the nutrients normally provided by meats, and in the case of vegans, eggs and dairy products, too. This means expanding your dietary range to include soy meats, beans and other legumes, nuts and seeds. Vegans will need to substitute dairy products with fortified soy milks and soy products. Supermarkets are making this easier by offering soy yogurts, custards and vegetarian alternatives to deli meats, sausages and hamburgers.

This book contains some vegetarian meal ideas, but most recipes can be suitably modified by replacing meat, poultry or fish with tofu, nutmeat or beans.

- Tofu is a good substitute in chicken and fish dishes. It needs to be cooked with some sauces or spices to promote a good flavour.
- Nutmeat and other prepared meat alternatives don't need to be cooked completely and should be added late in the cooking process.
- Vegans can substitute milk or evaporated milk in recipes with soy milk. Some thickening may be needed using cornflour mixed with a small amount of soy milk.

Gluten-free Eating

In some circles, a gluten-free diet has the reputation of being an alternative diet promoted for health and sporting benefits. This is undeserved. In fact, a gluten-free diet is a therapeutic eating pattern required by people with coeliac disease or gluten sensitivity. This medical condition means that people are unable to eat foods that contain the protein gluten. Strict adherence to this diet requires great dedication and, without care, food patterns may be inadequate in fibre and some micronutrients.

The following table summarises foods that contain gluten and alternatives that may be substituted in recipes. Gluten-sensitive athletes should seek professional advice from a sports dietitian to ensure that they are able to meet their nutritional goals. Local coeliac societies are the best source of updated information about suitable and unsuitable commercial food products.

Foods containing gluten	Wheat, wheatmeal, wheatgerm, wheat-based breakfast cereals, oatmeal, oatbran, barley, wheat-based pasta, semolina, farina, bread, biscuits, batter, crumbs, malt, malt extract, malt flavouring
Foods that may contain gluten	Modified starch, thickening agents 1400–1450, maltodextrin, hydrolysed protein, glucose, glucose syrup, caramel
Gluten-free foods	Rice, rice bran, rice flour, rice-based breakfast cereals, rice noodles and pasta, gluten-free bread, corn, maize flour (or cornflour), polenta, potato flour, buckwheat, arrowroot, chickpea flour (besan), lentils, lentil flour, sago, tapioca, amaranth

Lactose-free Diets

Lactose is the major sugar found in milk. Intolerance to lactose is often incorrectly self-diagnosed and dairy foods are often unnecessarily restricted. Some racial groups are more prone to lactose intolerance, and most people are encouraged to avoid excessive lactose intake during and for a few days after a gastric bug. However, lactose intolerance is usually a relative condition rather than an 'all or none' problem. What's more, not all dairy products contain large amounts of lactose. Milk is a high-lactose product, and a large bowl of ice cream can also upset the balance. There are, however, easy ways to avoid lactose overload and convert recipes for trouble-free cooking.

- Drink milk in servings of 250 mL (1 cup) or less and in conjunction with a meal.
- Try yogurt with active cultures.
- Choose dairy products which are naturally low in lactose, like cheese.
- Use lactase enzyme drops in milk or buy special low-lactose dairy products.
- Substitute dairy products with fortified soy milk, custards, yogurts or ice cream.

how to use this book

Consider this book a stepping stone towards great cooking. We hope that it will help you gain the confidence to become a winner in the kitchen. The recipes we have chosen were developed or adapted from AIS recipes to include most of the following features:

- Delicious taste
- High in carbohydrate for fuel and low in fat to keep you in shape
- Quick to prepare and cook — typically able to be on the table in 20–40 minutes
- A meal in one pot — a good balance of fuel, protein and vitamins and minerals in the one dish
- Basic techniques with few pots and pans to clean up
- Good for leftovers or freezing as a self-contained meal

We have also tried to use commonly found ingredients, and on occasions to take advantage of some convenience food products. The recipes demonstrate cooking techniques that can be applied in other settings, so we recommend you learn to experiment with them using our tips or suggestions for ingredient substitutes as a guide. The essential ingredients or steps are emphasised to make sure that you don't abandon the important parts of a recipe.

There is no such thing as a typical athlete. In suggesting serve sizes, we have generally catered for athletes with medium energy needs (4 serves to a recipe) and athletes with lesser energy needs (6 serves to a recipe). Nutrition information for each recipe is provided for these typical serve sizes. However, we all know athletes with huge energy needs, and it is possible that two of these athletes will eat a whole dish between them. Therefore, interpret the nutrition information with your needs in mind.

The following information is provided about each recipe:

- ENERGY VALUE
  although people think of energy as "get up and go", in fact is is simply the kilojoule or calorie content of the food

- CARBOHYDRATE CONTENT
  provided as grams (g) per serve

- FAT CONTENT
  provided as grams (g) per serve

- PROTEIN CONTENT
  provided as grams (g) per serve

- Special comments ~ may note content of iron, calcium vitamin C or zinc. We have also highlighted recipes which contain ingredients rich in phyto-chemicals. These are chemicals found in plant foods whose health promoting properties we are just beginning to discover.

Medals Scheme

Our system of medals helps you analyse the nutrient content of a meal and whether or not it is likely to help you meet your nutrition goals. The medals take into account the overall picture of a winning diet, and the role each recipe is likely to play.

- ● (Gold)   A real winner
- ● (Silver)   Nearly there
- ● (Bronze) Needs a little more work

Other Symbols

❋   Good for freezing

This symbol means that the recipe is suitable for freezing. Freeze the whole amount in an airtight container, or better still divide into single serves which can be quickly thawed and heated when required. Most meals can be left in the freezer for up to 2–3 months.

COOKING GOURMET MEALS

Most of the time, athletes want to eat no-fuss, quick and healthy meals, but there may be occasions when you want to entertain others or take a little more time and trouble with the meal preparation. Many of the recipes in this book are suitable for dinner parties and entertaining. With a little extra care, you can ensure your guests are impressed by your culinary skills.

- Use all fresh ingredients such as fresh herbs, fresh seafood or fish, and fresh vegetables.
- Take time to cut vegetables into attractive shapes, such as long thin strips.
- Nice plates and bowls enhance the presentation of meals, and set the table artistically to create the scene.
- Show flair when serving pasta sauces, risottos or stirfries. Rather than mixing or tossing all the ingredients together, serve the pasta, rice or noodles on the bowl or plate, then arrange the meat and vegetables in a colourful design on top.
- Use garnishes such as parsley, dill, coriander or other herbs. Experiment with more exotic varieties such as flat-leaf (Italian) parsley or gourmet lettuce mixes.

soups&
salads

soups & salads

Soups and salads are often misunderstood. To many athletes, they represent light and healthy eating, when in fact they are often short on fuel and high in fat. To others, they are lacking in substance and fussy to make. But when carefully chosen, soups and salads are actually great ways of delivering the goodness of vegetables, and with creative thinking they can easily be turned into main meals.

Preparing salads with oomph means combining vegetables with other foods that provide a good serve of carbohydrate and some protein. If you keep fatty ingredients and oily dressings at bay, salads become a tailor-made meal for athletes.

Soups, too, are under-utilised and traditionally treated as an appetiser to a meal. But hearty soups can easily become meals in themselves, and are ideal for a winter's lunch or quick evening meal. There is nothing nicer than thawing out after a chilly training session with a bowl of steaming, wholesome soup.

Another advantage of salads and soups is that they are enriched with antioxidants from the vegetables. Both soups and salads should also include carbohydrate-rich foods such as beans, rice, pasta or potatoes, but most will still fall short of meeting your fuel needs. Crusty fresh bread is a perfect partner for both soup and salads, and ensures that the meal will refuel you for your next work out.

In our preparation of these recipes, we have assumed that you will serve them with bread, so we have included a large roll or similarly sized bread choice in the analysis.

chicken & sweetcorn soup Serves 4-6

spray canola or olive oil
300 g chicken tenderloins
5 spring onions, thinly sliced
2 teaspoons minced ginger
pinch cayenne pepper
1½ litres (6 cups) MAGGI Chicken Stock
400 g can creamed corn
2 tablespoons chopped fresh parsley

Spray a nonstick frying pan with oil and heat. Cook the chicken for 5 minutes, turning occasionally, or until lightly browned and cooked through. Cool, cut into fine slices and set aside. Heat another spray of oil in a large saucepan. Add the spring onions and cook over medium heat for 2 minutes or until soft. Add the ginger and cayenne pepper and cook, stirring, for a further 1 minute. Add the stock, corn and cooked chicken to the pan. Bring to the boil, reduce the heat and simmer for 5 minutes. Stir in the parsley just before serving.

ANALYSIS (+ bread)	4		6	
Energy (kJ Cal)	1862	445	1241	297
● Carb (g)		64		43
● Prot (g)		30		20
● Fat (g)		7		5
● Fibre				
● Iron, Zinc				

HINT: *This soup is ideal with focaccia, herb or specialty bread.*

Preparation time: 5 minutes
Cooking time: 15 minutes

chicken & sweetcorn soup

" When I get the chance, I like to cook up a large batch of soup or other meals that are good for freezing. I freeze them in single or double serves rather than in a whole batch. It's great for emergencies and thaws quickly. The best part is that it's a whole meal in itself."

JACINTA VAN LINT ~ swimmer

seafood chowder Serves 4-6

spray canola or olive oil
1 onion, finely chopped
2 stalks celery, finely chopped
1 teaspoon minced garlic
900 g or 3 large potatoes, peeled and cut into small cubes
1 litre (4 cups) MAGGI Vegetable Stock
500 g white fish fillets, chopped
150 mL (²/₃ cup) can CARNATION Light and Creamy Evaporated Milk
freshly ground black pepper, to taste
2 tablespoons chopped fresh chives, optional

Spray a large saucepan with oil and heat. Add the onion and celery and cook over medium heat for 3 minutes or until soft. Add garlic and cook for 1 more minute. Add potato, stir to combine, then add the stock to the pan. Bring to the boil, then reduce heat and simmer, partially covered, for 20 minutes or until the potato is very tender. Add fish and simmer for 3–4 minutes or until the fish is cooked. Use a potato masher to mash the vegetables and fish until almost smooth or a food processor to puree the soup and make it very smooth. Stir in the milk, heat through and season with pepper to taste. Serve sprinkled with chives.

ANALYSIS (+ bread)	4		6	
Energy (kJ Cal)	2419	578	1613	385
● Carb (g)		82		55
● Prot (g)		43		29
● Fat (g)		8		5
● Vitamin C				
● Calcium, Iron, Zinc				

HINT: *Use 'floury' or all-purpose potatoes as they will break down during cooking and are easy to mash to a smooth consistency. This soup is great with damper, baguettes or sourdough bread.*

Preparation time: 10 minutes
Cooking time: 30 minutes

seafood chowder

hearty vegetable soup

pumpkin soup

"Cooking! That's something that I never had to deal with until recently. When I lived with my parents, there was always a meal on the table when I arrived home. Moving into shared accommodation with other athletes was a real shock. When I first moved out, I attended a couple of cooking nights with dietitians at the AIS. At first I was a little reluctant and viewed cooking as a chore. Now, it is something that I enjoy and I look forward to preparing some of my favourite dishes. I never ate stirfries at home, but now I find I have them regularly. Hokkien noodle dishes are my favourite. I love a one-dish dinner!" DAMIEN BURROUGHS ~ paralympian thrower

hearty vegetable soup Serves 4-6 ❄

spray of canola or olive oil
1 onion, chopped
2 teaspoons minced garlic
2 carrots, chopped
4 stalks celery, chopped
300 g peeled and chopped pumpkin
1 large zucchini (courgette), chopped
1 litre (4 cups) MAGGI Vegetable Stock
400 g can chopped tomatoes
1 teaspoon dried oregano
½ cup macaroni
300 g can butter beans, rinsed and drained
2 tablespoons chopped fresh parsley

Heat the oil in a large pan and cook the onion over medium heat for 3 minutes or until soft. Add the garlic and cook for 1 more minute. Add the carrot, celery, pumpkin and zucchini and stir into the onion mixture. Add the stock, tomatoes and oregano, and bring to the boil. Reduce the heat and simmer, partially covered, for 10 minutes. Add the pasta and cook a further 10 minutes or until the pasta and vegetables are tender. Stir in the butter beans and heat through. Just before serving, stir in the parsley.

ANALYSIS (+ bread)	4	6
Energy (kJ Cal) 1700 405	1130 270	
● Carb (g)	75	50
● Prot (g)	18	11
● Fat (g)	4	2
● Phyto-chemicals, Vitamin C		
● Fibre, Iron		

HINT: *This recipe can be adapted with 200 g trim lamb fillets (cut into thin strips and quickly stirfried over medium-high heat for 2–3 minutes) added to the soup at the end of cooking. Delicious with damper or crusty rolls.*

Preparation time: 15 minutes
Cooking time: 30 minutes

pumpkin soup Serves 4-6 ❄

spray of canola or olive oil
1 onion, finely chopped
1 kg butternut pumpkin, peeled and chopped into small cubes
750 mL (3 cups) MAGGI Chicken Stock
2 tablespoons chopped fresh parsley
250 mL (1 cup) CARNATION Light and Creamy Evaporated Milk
freshly ground black pepper, to taste

Spray a large pan with oil and heat. Add the onion and cook over medium heat for 3 minutes or until soft. Add the pumpkin and stock, bring to the boil. Reduce the heat slightly and simmer, partially covered, for 20 minutes or until the pumpkin is very soft. Puree the soup in a food processor until smooth, or mash thoroughly with a potato masher. Stir in the parsley and milk, and heat gently without boiling again. Season and serve.

ANALYSIS (+ bread)	4	6
Energy (kJ Cal) 1972 471	1315 314	
● Carb (g)	74	49
● Prot (g)	23	15
● Fat (g)	9	6
● Phyto-chemicals		

HINT: *To increase the nutritional value, add ³/4 cup red lentils with the pumpkin. This also thickens the soup, so add more stock or water if necessary. The combination of a pulse (lentils) with a grain (bread) creates a complete protein, making this a good vegetarian meal. This soup is best with a crusty Italian-style bread or a pull-apart loaf.*

Preparation time: 15 minutes
Cooking time: 25 minutes

pea & ham soup Serves 4-6 ❋

1 cup dried green split peas
spray canola or olive oil
1 onion, finely chopped
2 carrots, finely chopped
4 stalks celery, finely chopped
1½ litres (6 cups) MAGGI Chicken or Vegetable Stock
150 g lean sliced ham, chopped
2 tablespoons chopped fresh parsley
salt and freshly ground black pepper, to taste

Put the peas into a large bowl and cover generously with cold water. Stand for at least 6 hours or overnight, then drain well. Spray a large pan with oil and heat. Add the onion, carrot and celery and cook over medium heat for 3 minutes or until soft. Add the peas and stock, and bring to the boil. Reduce the heat and simmer, partially covered, for 30 minutes, or until the peas are very soft. Skim any froth while cooking. Stir in the ham and parsley, and heat through. Season to taste and serve.

ANALYSIS (+ bread)		4		6
Energy (kJ Cal)	1880	450	1255	300
● Carb (g)		69		46
● Prot (g)		25		16
● Fat (g)		8		5
● Phtyo-chemicals, Zinc				

HINT: *If you don't have time or have forgotten to soak the peas, add another 2 cups (500 mL) stock to the recipe and cook for an extra 30–40 minutes or until the peas are soft, before adding the ham. Serve with Turkish-style bread or pita bread.*

Preparation time: 10 minutes + soaking
Cooking time: 35 minutes

pea & ham soup

" When we moved into a house together, we didn't realise it would be so hard to get organised. Eventually, we made up a roster of the household duties, and this gets things done without disrupting the harmony. We all have different and busy timetables but when we do share a meal, you can be sure it is a healthy choice. "

BRYONY DUUS, AMY TAYLOR, GEORGETTE LEAKE & NATALIE THOMAS ~ soccer players

asian noodle soup Serves 4-6

spray of canola or olive oil
1 onion, finely chopped
1 teaspoon minced garlic
1 teaspoon minced ginger
1 teaspoon chopped red chilli
¼ teaspoon turmeric
375 mL (1½ cups) can CARNATION Light and Creamy Evaporated Milk
250 mL (1 cup) MAGGI Chicken Stock
½ teaspoon coconut essence
250 g firm tofu, cut into cubes
300 g green (raw) prawns, peeled and deveined
200 g thin egg noodles
100 g snow peas, sliced
125 g bean sprouts
¼ cup fresh coriander leaves

Spray a large pan with oil and heat. Add the onion and cook over medium heat for 3 minutes or until soft. Add the garlic, ginger, chilli and turmeric and stirfry for about 30 seconds. Gradually add the milk and stock to the pan, stirring to scrape the onion and spices from the bottom. Stir in the essence. Bring to the boil, reduce the heat slightly then add the tofu and prawns. Simmer for 2–3 minutes or until the prawns are opaque. Meanwhile, cook the noodles following the packet instructions and divide between 4 bowls. Pour the soup over, dividing the tofu and prawns evenly, and top with snow peas, sprouts and coriander.

ANALYSIS (+ bread)		4		6
Energy (kJ Cal)	2227	532	1484	355
● Carb (g)		74		50
● Prot (g)		40		27
● Fat (g)		9		6
● Calcium, Iron, Zinc				
● Phyto-chemicals				

HINT: *This soup is delicious with a French bread stick.*

Preparation time: 20 minutes
Cooking time: 10 minutes

asian noodle soup

chicken & pasta salad

gado gado with noodles

"I share the cooking with my girlfriend. I like to have fresh vegies with every meal and to mix them into the recipe. It makes the meal more interesting and I often end up eating things that I don't like by themselves. We even put brussels sprouts into shepherd's pie. It's fun to go outside the mandatory carrots and beans and get some interesting flavours going. We eat a huge variety. My cooking skills have picked up heaps and I really enjoy it." BILL KIRBY ~ swimmer

chicken & pasta salad Serves 4-6

500 g spiral pasta
2 cups frozen vegetables (peas, corn and diced carrot)
1 barbecued chicken
2 stalks celery, chopped
125 g (½ cup) low-fat mayonnaise
125 g (½ cup) low-fat natural yogurt
1 tablespoon lemon juice
1 teaspoon finely grated lemon rind
2 tablespoons chopped fresh dill, optional
freshly ground black pepper, to taste

Cook the pasta in a large pan of boiling water until al dente. Rinse under cold water and drain well. Cook the vegetables according to packet instructions. Remove the meat (minus skin and fat) from the chicken and chop it roughly. Combine the pasta, vegetables, chicken and celery in a large bowl. Mix the mayonnaise, yogurt, lemon juice, rind and dill in a small bowl, then add to the pasta mixture. Toss to mix the dressing through the salad and season to taste.

ANALYSIS	4	6
Energy (kJ Cal)	3380 807	2253 538
● Carb (g)	102	68
● Prot (g)	63	42
● Fat (g)	15	10
● Iron, Zinc		

Preparation time: 15 minutes
Cooking time: 10 minutes

gado gado with noodles Serves 4-6

PEANUT SAUCE
3 tablespoons peanut butter
2 teaspoons curry powder
1 tablespoon MAGGI Fish Sauce
1 tablespoon soy sauce
2 tablespoons MAGGI Sweet Chilli Sauce
1 tablespoon chopped lemongrass
185 mL (¾ cup) CARNATION Light and Creamy Evaporated Milk

1 cup broccoli florets
1 carrot, thinly sliced
1 cup shredded cabbage
60 g snow peas
700 g Hokkien noodles
1 cup bean sprouts
4 boiled eggs, quartered
100 g firm tofu, chopped
4 spring onions, sliced

To make the peanut sauce, combine all the ingredients in a small saucepan and bring to the boil. Reduce heat and simmer for 1 minute, stirring constantly, then set aside. Place the broccoli and carrot in a large heatproof bowl and cover with boiling water. Leave to stand for 2 minutes, then drain and rinse under cold running water until cool. Drain well. Repeat with the cabbage and snow peas, but only stand them in boiling water for 20 seconds. Put the noodles in a large heatproof bowl and cover with boiling water. Gently prise them apart with two forks until the strands separate. Drain well. Divide the noodles between serving dishes, topped with the vegetables, bean sprouts, boiled eggs and tofu. Drizzle the warm peanut sauce over the top, and sprinkle with spring onions.

ANALYSIS	4	6
Energy (kJ Cal)	3687 881	2458 587
● Carb (g)	126	84
● Prot (g)	42	28
Fat (g)	23	15
● Phyto-chemicals, Vitamin C		
● Calcium, Iron		

Preparation time: 20 minutes
Cooking time: 2 minutes

rice, pork & mango salad Serves 4-6

500 g pork fillets, trimmed
spray of canola or olive oil
1 teaspoon minced ginger
2 tablespoons hoisin sauce
400 g can mango slices
1 Lebanese cucumber
2 cups cooked long-grain rice
1 small red capsicum, chopped
125 mL (½ cup) lemon juice
2 tablespoons honey
1 teaspoon chopped fresh chilli
salt and freshly ground black pepper, to taste
300 g mixed salad greens

Cut the pork into strips. Spray a nonstick wok or frying pan with oil and heat. Stirfry the pork in 2 batches for 3 minutes each. Add the ginger and hoisin sauce to the pork and toss to combine. Drain the mangoes and reserve ⅓ cup of the juice. Cut the cucumber in half lengthways, then into slices, and combine with the rice and capsicum. In a small bowl or jug, mix together the mango juice, lemon juice, honey and chilli. Pour over the rice salad, toss to combine and season to taste. Gently stir the mango slices and pork through the rice. Serve on a bed of salad greens.

ANALYSIS		4	6
Energy (kJ Cal)		2177 520	1451 347
● Carb (g)		71	47
● Prot (g)		39	26
● Fat (g)		9	6
● Iron, Vitamin C, Zinc			

HINT: *If you want to use fresh mango in season instead of canned, replace the reserved mango juice with the same amount of fresh orange juice.*

Preparation time: 10 minutes
Cooking time: 6 minutes

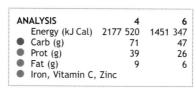
rice, pork & mango salad

" You wouldn't have thought when I was at the AIS that I would become such a foodie. But I really love to cook now. My wife and I have different schedules so I need to be able to look after myself. I plan the day's eating each morning and do the shopping on the way home from the pool. I know that's not as efficient as doing a weekly shop, but I have the time and I really enjoy fresh ingredients."

SCOTT MILLER ~ swimmer

spicy beef & noodle salad Serves 4-6

spray of canola or olive oil
300 g rump steak
170 mL (⅔ cup) low-fat French dressing
2 tablespoons MAGGI Sweet Chilli Sauce
1 tablespoon finely chopped mint or basil
700 g Hokkien noodles
1 green capsicum, sliced
1 red capsicum, sliced
150 g snow peas, halved
1 punnet cherry tomatoes, halved
1 Lebanese cucumber, sliced

Spray a nonstick frying pan with oil and heat. Cook the steak over medium-high heat for 3 minutes on each side, turning once only. Remove from the pan, cover with foil and set aside for 5 minutes before cutting into thin slices. Combine the dressing, the sweet chilli sauce and the mint in a small jug or bowl. Put the noodles in a large heatproof bowl and cover with boiling water. Gently prise them apart with two forks until the strands separate. Drain well. While the noodles are still warm, place with the vegetables and sliced beef in a large bowl, pour the dressing over and gently combine. Serve immediately.

ANALYSIS		4	6
Energy (kJ Cal)		3041 727	2028 484
● Carb (g)		119	79
● Prot (g)		42	28
● Fat (g)		8	6
● Iron, Vitamin C, Zinc			

HINT: *You can also replace the beef with chicken. Either stirfry 300 g chicken breast fillet, cut into strips, or use the meat from half a barbecue chicken, avoiding any skin or fat.*

Preparation time: 15 minutes
Cooking time: 6 minutes

spicy beef & noodle salad

spicy bean burritos

lamb & spinach salad

"I always plan cooking classes into the AIS basketball curriculum for the year. The boys really enjoy a night away from the dining hall, and they go home for the holidays eager to practise their new cooking skills for their families. The skills learned at the classes come in handy when they leave the Institute to take up contracts in the NBL or overseas. It's hard to learn to fend for yourself when you've had everything done for you." FRANK ARSEGO ~ basketball coach

spicy bean burritos Serves 2-4

FILLING
spray of canola or olive oil
1 onion, finely chopped
1 teaspoon ground cumin
1 teaspoon ground coriander
440 g can red kidney beans, rinsed and drained
400 g can crushed tomatoes
2 tablespoons tomato paste
2 teaspoons MAGGI Chilli Sauce

8 flour tortillas
4 large lettuce leaves, shredded
3 tomatoes, chopped
½ cup grated reduced-fat tasty cheese
4 tablespoons low-fat natural yogurt

To make the filling, spray a nonstick frying pan with oil and heat. Add the onion and cook over medium heat for 3 minutes or until soft. Add spices and cook, stirring, for 1 minute. Add the beans, tomatoes, tomato paste and chilli sauce. Bring to the boil, reduce the heat and simmer for 4 minutes or until thickened slightly. To serve, divide the filling into four and place on a double layer of tortillas. Roll up and top with lettuce, tomato, cheese and yogurt.

ANALYSIS		2		4
Energy (kJ Cal)	4203	1004	2101	502
● Carb (g)		159		80
● Prot (g)		51		25
● Fat (g)		17		9
● Iron				
● Calcium, Fibre, Phyto-chemicals, Zinc				

Preparation time: 15 minutes
Cooking time: 10 minutes

lamb & spinach salad Serves 4-6

500 g baby potatoes
spray of canola or olive oil
300 g trim lamb fillet
125 g English spinach leaves
250 g punnet cherry tomatoes, halved
1 small red onion, cut into thin wedges
2 tablespoons lemon juice
freshly ground black pepper, to taste

Cook the potatoes in a large pan of boiling water for 10–15 minutes or until tender, but do not overcook. Drain well, cool until just warm and then cut in half. Meanwhile, spray a nonstick frying pan with oil and heat. Add the lamb fillet and cook for 5 minutes on each side. Transfer to a plate, cover loosely with foil and set aside for 5 minutes, then cut into thin slices. Toss the spinach leaves, tomatoes, onion and warm potatoes with the lemon juice. Arrange on serving plates, and top with the sliced lamb. Season to taste, and serve.

ANALYSIS		4		6
Energy (kJ Cal)	1874	448	1249	298
● Carb (g)		66		44
● Prot (g)		29		19
● Fat (g)		7		5
● Iron, Vitamin C, Zinc				

HINT: *English spinach leaves are available loose from most greengrocers and supermarkets. Wash and dry well before use. You can also use rocket, or combine rocket and spinach, for a spicier flavour.*

Preparation time: 10 minutes
Cooking time: 15 minutes

rice

rice

Rice is a great source of carbohydrate, but it is often under-utilised by athletes who are afraid that it is messy and time consuming to cook.

The easiest way to cook rice is simply by boiling. This is pretty foolproof, provided you use a large saucepan, and plenty of water — allow about 2 litres (8 cups) water to cook 1 cup of rice. Bring to the boil, then add the rice and give it a brief stir to distribute the grains. Start timing when the water begins to boil again. Long, medium and short grain rice will all take approximately the same amount of time to cook — about 12–15 minutes. Scoop out a few grains after 12 minutes, cool slightly and taste to see if the rice is cooked to your liking. If not, cook a little longer. Brown rice will take longer, about 25–30 minutes. Once cooked, stand a large sieve or colander over the sink and pour in the rice to drain.

Another common way to cook rice is by the absorption method. This can be a little tricky until you get the hang of it but produces light, fluffy rice which is less likey to be gluggy. It is the preferred way to cook basmati and jasmine rice, retaining the characteristic fragrance of those types of rice.

To cook rice by absorption, place the rice and water into a saucepan, using a ratio of 1 cup rice to 375 mL (1½ cups) water, and bring to the boil. Cover with a tight-fitting lid, and reduce the heat to very low — as low as you possibly can. Cook for about 10 minutes, then turn off the heat and leave to stand for 5 minutes. Try to resist lifting the lid from the saucepan before the required time, as this will cause loss of steam which you need to cook the rice. Uncover and fluff up the grains with a fork before serving.

To cook rice in the microwave, combine rice and water in a ratio of 1 cup rice to 500 mL (2 cups) water, in a microwave-safe bowl. Cook on HIGH for 12–14 minutes. Don't cover the bowl or the water will boil over. (Based on an 850 watt microwave: higher wattages will require less time, and lower ones will need more.)

hints & tips

Fried rice is best made with rice cooked a day in advance and left, covered in a bowl, in the fridge overnight. This ensures the rice is quite 'dry', so the fried rice will have separate grains and not be gluggy. If you haven't cooked the rice the day before, cook it as far in advance as possible, and after draining, spread the rice onto a plate, and refrigerate until needed.

Store cooked rice in the freezer, for up to 2 months, either in a large bag or single serves. Expel as much air as possible from the bag before sealing tightly.

For something a little different and really quick, try couscous. To prepare, combine equal parts of couscous and boiling water in a heatproof bowl or a saucepan, and cover with a tightly fitting lid. Leave to stand for 5 minutes, then fluff up the grains with a fork and serve. One cup of dry couscous makes about 2¾ cups cooked.

Arborio is an Italian rice with particular characteristics which makes it the only type of rice suitable to make risotto (apart from a couple of fairly obscure types — which are not available at the supermarket). Risotto should be creamy but not gluggy, with the grains of rice still slightly al dente.

Try basmati rice for curries and Indian dishes, and jasmine with stirfries and Thai curries. Each has a subtle fragrance which adds an extra dimension to the meal.

A rice cooker takes all the guesswork out of cooking rice and ensures perfect results every time. They are a little expensive, but if you eat a lot of rice, or cook regularly for a crowd, they can be an invaluable tool.

Rice which can be 'cooked' in the fridge has been par-cooked. Just combine with water and leave in the fridge until absorbed. It's ideal for a quick fried rice.

Brown rice is long or medium grain rice with the outer husk removed, but no further processing. It is more nutritious than white rice, being a 'whole' grain, and is higher in fibre. It does take significantly longer to cook, however, so needs some forward planning.

Wild rice is not technically a rice, but the seed of a grass from North America. It has a nutty, earthy flavour, and is not normally eaten in great volume — use in stuffings, or after cooking combine with cooked brown or white rice. It is relatively expensive but a little goes a long way.

baked beef risotto Serves 3-4

spray canola or olive oil
1 onion, finely chopped
2 teaspoons minced garlic
350 g lean beef mince
1½ cups arborio rice
1 litre (4 cups) MAGGI Beef Stock
150 g baby spinach leaves
400 g sweet potato (kumera), cut into small cubes
1 tablespoon finely grated Parmesan cheese
freshly ground black pepper, to taste

Preheat the oven to moderate (180°C or 350°F). Spray a large pan with oil and heat. Cook the onion, garlic and mince for about 5 minutes or until browned, breaking up any lumps of mince with a fork. Add the rice and stir until well combined. Stir in the stock, spinach and sweet potato and bring to the boil. Transfer the mixture to a 2 litre (8 cup) capacity ovenproof dish. Cover and bake for 20 minutes. Remove the lid from the dish, stir the risotto well and return to the oven to cook, uncovered, for a further 10 minutes or until the rice is tender and the stock has been absorbed. Stir in the Parmesan cheese and season to taste. Serve immediately.

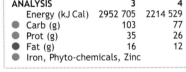

ANALYSIS		3	4
	Energy (kJ Cal)	2952 705	2214 529
●	Carb (g)	103	77
●	Prot (g)	35	26
●	Fat (g)	16	12
●	Iron, Phyto-chemicals, Zinc		

Preparation time: 10 minutes
Cooking time: 35 minutes

baked beef risotto

rice with tofu Serves 3-4

200 g firm tofu, chopped
80 mL (⅓ cup) MAGGI Stir-Fry Sauce
2 tablespoons soy sauce
spray of canola or olive oil
5 spring onions, sliced diagonally
1 red capsicum, sliced
425 g can baby corn, drained and chopped
200 g green beans, sliced diagonally
4 cups cooked long-grain rice

Place the tofu in a small bowl and add the stirfry sauce and soy sauce. Toss to coat and set aside until required. Spray a wok or large frying pan with oil and heat. Add spring onions, capsicum, corn and beans and stirfry for 2–3 minutes or until vegetables are tender but still crisp. Add the tofu (with all the sauce) and stirfry for 2–3 minutes or until heated through. Serve with the rice, adding more soy sauce to taste.

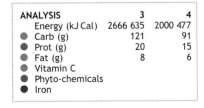

ANALYSIS		3	4
	Energy (kJ Cal)	2666 635	2000 477
●	Carb (g)	121	91
●	Prot (g)	20	15
●	Fat (g)	8	6
●	Vitamin C		
●	Phyto-chemicals		
●	Iron		

HINT: *This is a vegetarian dish in which tofu is used as a meat alternative. The vitamin C content helps to enhance iron absorption.*

Preparation time: 10 minutes
Cooking time: 6 minutes

" I follow a vegetarian eating plan myself, so I take every opportunity to introduce vegetarian 'alternatives' to athletes in our cooking classes. Tofu is a food that most athletes have heard about, but never tried. As soon as I mention it at a cooking night, there are always a couple of athletes who instantly screw up their noses. I always get a real kick when an athlete who is apprehensive about eating tofu ends up raving about how good the meal was."

GREG COX ~ sports dietitian

rice with tofu

seafood paella

microwave leek & herb risotto

" During my university studies as a dietitian, I was voted by my classmates as the most unlikely to succeed in the kitchen. In fact, I didn't start cooking until I was 22! Because of this late beginning, I have empathy for all of those athletes I have worked with during their first tentative steps in the kitchen. I realise that in order to build 'kitchen confidence', success must come before failure. Many of these recipes I have completed successfully with my own hands. I believe that the introduction of new recipes and cooking methods in a positive environment is the most enduring form of nutrition education. " BEN DESBROW ~ sports dietitian

seafood paella Serves 3-4

12 mussels
300 g medium green (raw) prawns
200 g scallops
spray canola or olive oil
1 onion, chopped
2 teaspoons minced garlic
pinch cayenne pepper
1 red capsicum, chopped
1 green capsicum, chopped
1½ cups long-grain rice
400 g can crushed tomatoes
250 mL (1 cup) MAGGI Chicken Stock
1 cup frozen peas

Scrub the mussel shells and remove the beards. Place into a large pan with ½ cup water. Cover and cook over medium heat for 5 minutes, shaking the pan occasionally. Discard any mussels which do not open in this time. Peel and devein the prawns, leaving the tails intact. Spray a large nonstick frying pan with oil and heat. Add the prawns and scallops and cook over high heat for about 2 minutes or until the flesh turns white. Remove from the pan and set aside. Add the onion to the pan and cook over medium heat for 3 minutes or until soft. Stir in the garlic and cayenne, then the capsicum and rice, and cook, stirring constantly, for a further 2 minutes. Add the tomatoes, stock and peas and stir through. Bring paella to the boil then reduce the heat to very low and cover tightly. Cook for 20 minutes or until the rice is just tender and the stock is almost all absorbed. Add the prawns, scallops and mussels to the rice, and very gently stir through. Cover and cook for a further 3 minutes or until the seafood is heated through. Serve immediately.

ANALYSIS		3	4
Energy (kJ Cal)	2419	578	1815 433
● Carb (g)		92	70
● Prot (g)		41	31
● Fat (g)		5	3
● Iron, Vitamin C, Zinc			
● Phyto-chemicals			

HINT: *A "pinch" of something usually means less than a ¼ teaspoon. To avoid getting the hot cayenne on your fingers, lift it with the tip of a pointed knife to obtain the small amount required.*

Preparation time: 15 minutes
Cooking time: 35 minutes

microwave leek & herb risotto Serves 3-4

spray canola or olive oil
2 medium leeks, finely sliced
1½ cups arborio rice
1 litre (4 cups) MAGGI Chicken or Vegetable Stock
½ cup grated reduced-fat tasty cheese
2 tablespoons chopped fresh parsley
1 teaspoon mixed dried herbs
2 teaspoons finely grated lemon rind

Place the oil and leek in a large straight-sided microwave dish. Cook, uncovered, on HIGH for 4 minutes. Stir in the rice and cook, uncovered, on HIGH for a further 4 minutes. Add the chicken stock and cook, uncovered, on HIGH for 9 minutes. Remove from the microwave, stir well and cook, uncovered, on HIGH for another 9 minutes. If the liquid hasn't fully absorbed into the rice, cook for another minute or so. Remove from the microwave. Stir in the cheese, herbs and lemon rind and serve immediately.

ANALYSIS		3	4
Energy (kJ Cal)	2032	486	1525 364
● Carb (g)		85	63
● Prot (g)		16	12
● Fat (g)		9	8
● Calcium			

HINT: *Serve with a salad or add extra vegetables such as corn kernels, capsicum and broccoli for extra vitamins, and with pita or Lebanese bread to boost the carbohydrate level.*

Preparation time: 10 minutes
Cooking time: 25 minutes

lamb & pumpkin pilaf   Serves 3-4

spray canola or olive oil
400 g lean lamb, cut into thin strips
1 medium onion, finely chopped
2 teaspoons ground coriander
2 teaspoons ground cumin
1½ cups basmati rice
400 g pumpkin, peeled and cut into 1 cm cubes
150 g green beans, cut into 2 cm lengths
625 mL (2½ cups) MAGGI Chicken Stock

Spray a large pan with oil and heat. Stirfry the meat in two batches. Transfer to a plate, cover and set aside. Cook the onion over medium-low heat for about 5 minutes or until very soft and lightly golden. Add the spices and stir for about 30 seconds or until fragrant. Add the rice and stir to coat with the onion mixture. Add the pumpkin, beans and stock and stir until well combined. Cover with a tight-fitting lid and bring to the boil. Reduce the heat to very low, and cook for 12 minutes or until all the stock is absorbed. Turn off the heat and stand for 5 minutes or until the rice is tender. Return the meat to the pan, use a fork to mix through and fluff up the rice. Serve immediately.

ANALYSIS	3	4
Energy (kJ Cal)	2570 614	1927 460
● Carb (g)	93	70
● Prot (g)	41	30
● Fat (g)	8	6
● Iron, Phyto-chemicals, Zinc		

HINT: *To check the rice, remove the lid only very briefly so that the moisture needed to cook the rice is not lost.*

Preparation time: 15 minutes
Cooking time: 30 minutes

lamb & pumpkin pilaf

"Risotto is my favourite dish. As long as you have stock and arborio rice you can add any combination of ingredients to make a delicious meal. I love meals where you throw everything into a pot, give the occasional stir and 20–30 minutes later you have a delicious creation."

MICHELLE MINEHAN ~ sports dietitian

chilli chicken & rice   Serves 3-4

spray canola or olive oil
1 red onion, finely sliced
300 g chicken mince
2 teaspoons minced garlic
2 teaspoons minced ginger
1 red capsicum, finely chopped
1 tablespoon MAGGI Fish Sauce
1–2 tablespoons MAGGI Sweet Chilli Sauce, to taste
2 tablespoons chopped fresh coriander
5 cups cooked long-grain white rice
12 iceberg lettuce leaves

Spray a nonstick wok or frying pan with oil and heat. Add the onion and cook for about 2 minutes or until just soft. Add the chicken mince, garlic and ginger and cook for about 5 minutes or until browned, breaking up lumps of mince with a wooden spoon. Add the capsicum and cook for 3 minutes more, stirring frequently. Add the fish sauce and sweet chilli sauce, to taste. Stir in the coriander. To serve, spoon the chicken mixture and rice into the lettuce leaves and roll up to eat with your fingers.

ANALYSIS	3	4
Energy (kJ Cal)	2686 642	1611 385
● Carb	112	67
● Prot	35	21
● Fat	5	4
● Vitamin C		
● Iron, Zinc		

HINT: *Use lavash or mountain bread instead of lettuce to wrap up the mixture to add extra carbohydrate. Add other vegetables (such as sliced zucchini, mushrooms, corn) to the mixture to make a complete meal.*

Preparation time: 10 minutes
Cooking time: 10 minutes

chilli chicken & rice

fried rice & vegetables

chicken & corn risotto

"Coach makes sure we never wander too far from our weight class. Sure we have to worry about weight, but we also have to keep pace with the energy demands of training. When we come into camp at the AIS, we often train three times a day, either running, sparring, or at the gym. Managing meals and snacks around training sessions can become difficult, particularly as you want to feel ready for your next training session. Making the right snack choices is important and this cookbook includes a few of our favourite recipes and snack ideas. Our golden rule for cooking is easy to prepare, easy to eat." AIS boxing team

fried rice & vegetables   Serves 3-4

spray canola or olive oil
1 egg, lightly beaten
1 onion, finely chopped
1 green capsicum, chopped
200 g button mushrooms, sliced
1½ cups finely shredded cabbage
1 large carrot, grated or thinly sliced
1 cup snow pea sprouts
5 cups cooked brown rice
1 tablespoon chopped fresh parsley
soy sauce, to taste

Spray a nonstick wok or frying pan with oil and heat. Add the egg and swirl to create a thin omelette. When the egg has set and cooked, turn out, cool, and cut into short, thin strips. Spray the wok or frying pan with oil and heat again. Add the onion and capsicum and cook over moderately high heat for 2 minutes, stirring constantly. Add remaining vegetables and stirfry for a further 2 minutes or until the vegetables are just softened. Add the rice and stir until well combined and heated through. Stir through the parsley and egg, and season with soy sauce to taste.

ANALYSIS		3	4
Energy (kJ Cal)	2590	618	1940 463
● Carb (g)		100	75
● Prot (g)		35	26
● Fat (g)		7	5
● Vitamin C			
● Phyto-chemicals			

HINT: *This recipe is a great way to use up any vegetables you have on hand. You could replace the egg with chopped tofu.*

Preparation time: 15 minutes
Cooking time: 10 minutes

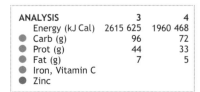

chicken & corn risotto   Serves 3-4

spray canola or olive oil
1 onion, finely chopped
1½ cups arborio rice
400 g chicken breast fillet, cut into strips
425 g can baby corn cuts, drained
1 small red capsicum, chopped
1 cup frozen peas
750 mL (3 cups) MAGGI Chicken Stock
½ cup tomato-based pasta sauce
2 tablespoons chopped fresh basil
2 tablespoons chopped fresh parsley
freshly ground black pepper, to taste

Spray a large pan with oil and heat. Add the onion, rice, chicken, corn, capsicum and peas. Cook, stirring, over medium heat for 2 minutes. Add the stock and pasta sauce and stir until well combined. Bring to the boil, reduce the heat to low and simmer, covered, for 20-25 minutes. Stir frequently until the rice is tender and the liquid is almost all absorbed. Remove from heat and stand, covered, for 5 minutes. Stir in the herbs and season to taste before serving.

ANALYSIS		3	4
Energy (kJ Cal)	2615	625	1960 468
● Carb (g)		96	72
● Prot (g)		44	33
● Fat (g)		7	5
● Iron, Vitamin C			
● Zinc			

HINT: *Always measure liquid accurately using proper measuring cups (available at supermarkets), not tea or coffee cups, so the rice cooks correctly. You can also replace the frozen peas with broccoli.*

Preparation time: 15 minutes
Cooking time: 30 minutes

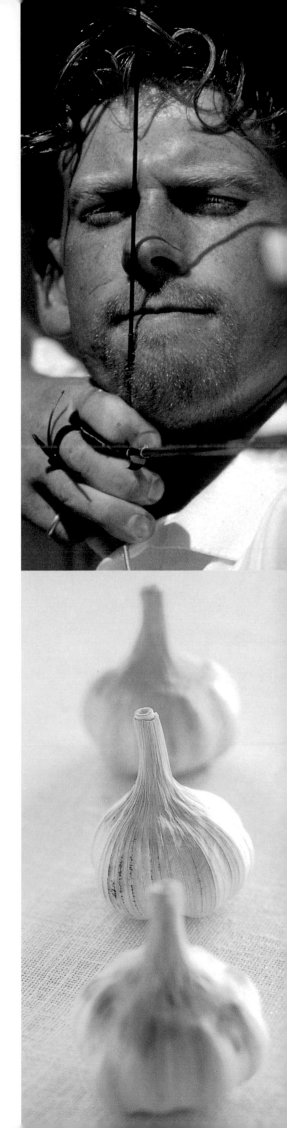

pasta

pasta

There are few athletes who aren't aware that pasta is a great source of carbohydrates. But for a pasta meal to be ideal, it is important to keep the components balanced. Many athletes eat too much of the fatty sauce instead of the pasta, or overload on extra cheese. This is particularly true of lasagne. Others forget to include vegetables altogether.

Cooking a pasta meal at home has been made very easy by the increasing availability of quality commercial pasta sauces. Many of the prepared tomato-based sauces are low in fat, and taste great on their own or when used as a base for a fancier sauce you make yourself. But make sure you read the labels — you will find that many of the commercially available creamy pasta bakes and white sauces are a hidden source of fat.

The pasta sauces in this book are low in fat and quick to prepare. If fresh vegetables aren't already included in the sauce recipe, make sure you serve the meal with a quick salad or some steamed vegetables for an extra vitamin boost and use wholemeal pasta to increase your fibre intake.

Certain types of pasta are often matched with sauces according to the thickness of the sauce and the intensity of the flavours, but you can interchange the types recommended for the recipes in this book. Don't be afraid to use up what's in the pantry, or to throw in additional vegetables.

Lasagnes are not always ideal for busy athletes. These dishes are often high in fat due to the meat, creamy sauces and cheese, and there's not much carbohydrate in the few sheets of pasta between. Exchange the traditional bechamel (white) sauce for tasty low-fat options such as ricotta and tomato pasta sauces and always use cheese sparingly — just a sprinkle to add a golden finish. You can also make a quick, low-fat white sauce by thickening skim milk with cornflour and adding a small amount of reduced-fat cheese.

hints & tips

Always start boiling the water for the pasta as your first step. Use a big saucepan that will hold enough water to cover the pasta. To speed up the boiling process, start with hot water from the tap and put the lid on the saucepan until the water is bubbling.

Only add the pasta when the water is thoroughly boiling then stir to prevent it sticking. There's no need to add oil or salt. Don't overcook pasta — it should be al dente or just tender. Some types, like gnocchi and fresh pasta, only take a few minutes to cook and will float to the top of the water when ready.

When the pasta is cooked, drain in a colander and rinse under a running tap with hot water (especially sticky pastas like gnocchi and fettucine). The pasta may be placed back in the saucepan and covered until you are ready to serve.

Including vegetables in the sauce ensures you have a balanced meal and means all your cooking can be done in two saucepans so it saves on cleaning up, too.

Traditional creamy-style sauces are often made with high-fat ingredients such as butter, cream or cheese. For a healthier alternative use CARNATION Light and Creamy Evaporated Milk thickened with cornflour.

Lasagnes can take about 2 hours to cook, but the recipes in this book cut down the time significantly by using convenience foods such as fresh lasagne sheets and prepared pasta sauces. Fresh lasagne sheets reduce baking time by 20–30 minutes. They are soft and flexible, so you can fit more layers in the dish. Keeping the sauce thin and adding pasta layers will also help to boost the carbohydrate content.

Shorten your cooking time when using dried lasagne sheets by soaking the pasta in boiling water for a few minutes while you make the sauce or filling.

Make sure meat lasagnes are balanced meals by serving with vegetables or salad and crusty fresh bread for an extra fuel boost. Alternatively, halve the amount of meat in the recipe and replace it with vegetables.

Increase the carbohydrate content of lasagne by using double pasta layers (works well with chunky sauces) or add beans (kidney, soy or baked), corn or potato to the filling.

penne with chicken & feta Serves 4-6

500 g penne
spray of canola or olive oil
500 g or two skinless chicken breast fillets, cut into thin strips
1 small onion, finely chopped
2 teaspoons minced garlic
125 mL (½ cup) MAGGI Chicken Stock
825 g can crushed tomatoes
1 tablespoon tomato paste
salt and freshly ground black pepper, to taste
60 g feta cheese, cut into small cubes
¼ cup fresh basil leaves (optional)

Start cooking the pasta in a large saucepan of boiling water. Spray a nonstick frying pan or wok with oil and heat. Cook the chicken over medium–high heat for about 5 minutes or until browned. Remove from the pan and set aside. Add the onion to the pan and cook over medium heat for 3 minutes or until soft. Add the garlic and cook for 1 minute more. Add the stock, tomatoes and tomato paste, and bring to the boil. Reduce heat slightly, and simmer for 5 minutes, stirring occasionally. Return the chicken to the pan and heat through. Season to taste. When the pasta is al dente, drain and toss with the sauce to combine. Just before serving, stir the feta and basil into the sauce. Serve immediately with salad.

ANALYSIS	4	6
Energy (kJ Cal)	2790 567	1862 445
⬤ Carb (g)	96	64
⬤ Prot (g)	47	31
⬤ Fat (g)	10	6
⬤ Iron		
⬤ Phyto-chemicals, Zinc		

HINT: *Feta cheese is available in packets, but it is also sold by weight from delicatessens or the supermarket deli counter, which is convenient as you can buy just the amount you need.*

Preparation time: 15 minutes
Cooking time: 15 minutes

penne with chicken & feta

" We did cooking classes on the Pan Pac swimming camp and it was good fun. It was great to learn that you can make things that taste so good, and are so good for you, so quickly. And there was hardly anything to clean up."

ELLI OVERTON ~ swimmer

penne with ratatouille Serves 4-6 ❄ *(sauce only)*

500 g penne
2 tablespoons olive oil
1 onion, chopped
2 teaspoons minced garlic
1 red capsicum, chopped
2 zucchini (courgette), sliced
2 slender eggplant (aubergine), sliced
825 g can crushed tomatoes or 4 chopped tomatoes
2 tablespoons chopped fresh parsley
1 tablespoon capers (optional)
freshly ground black pepper, to taste

Start cooking the penne in a large saucepan of boiling water. Heat the oil in a large frying pan. Add the onion and cook for 3 minutes over medium heat until lightly golden, then add the garlic and cook for 1 minute more. Add the capsicum and zucchini to the pan and cook, stirring regularly, for 2 minutes or until they begin to soften. Add the eggplant and stir to combine. Add the tomatoes to the pan, bring to the boil and reduce the heat to low. Simmer, covered, for 15 minutes, stirring occasionally, until the vegetables are soft. Uncover and cook, stirring frequently, for a further 5 minutes or until thickened slightly. Stir in the parsley and capers and season to taste. When the pasta is al dente, drain and serve tossed through the ratatouille.

ANALYSIS	4	6
Energy (kJ Cal)	2330 550	1369 327
⬤ Carb (g)	98	66
⬤ Prot (g)	17	12
⬤ Fat (g)	10	2
⬤ Vitamin C		
⬤ Fibre, Phyto-chemicals		

HINT: *This vegetarian dish does not include a meat substitute. If you follow a vegetarian lifestyle, make sure that other meals in the week include meat alternatives, such as legumes, tofu or soy products.*

Preparation time: 15 minutes
Cooking time: 30 minutes

penne with ratatouille

spirals with chicken & mushrooms

fettucine with fresh tomato & chickpeas

" It was a good idea to have a cooking class instead of a nutrition lecture on our visit to the AIS. We made lasagnes, both meat and vegetarian versions, a tofu stirfry, and chocolate brownies. The recipes were really easy and fast, and they tasted great. It was good to learn practical stuff. "

ironmen athletes

spirals with chicken & mushrooms Serves 4-6

500 g spiral pasta
spray of canola or olive oil
500 g or two skinless chicken breast fillets, chopped into small cubes
200 g button mushrooms, quartered
5 spring onions, sliced
1½ tablespoons cornflour
375 mL can CARNATION Light and Creamy Evaporated Milk
125 mL (½ cup) MAGGI Chicken Stock
freshly ground black pepper, to taste

Start cooking the spirals in a large saucepan of boiling water. Spray a nonstick frying pan or wok with oil and heat. Cook the chicken over high heat for about 5 minutes or until browned. Remove from the pan and set aside. Reduce the heat to medium, add the mushrooms and spring onions to the pan and cook, stirring frequently, for 3 minutes or until soft. Put cornflour into a small bowl and gradually add ⅓ cup (80 mL) milk, stirring until smooth. Pour the remaining milk and chicken stock into the pan, then gradually add the cornflour mixture, stirring constantly. Keep stirring until the sauce boils and thickens. Season to taste. Stir the chicken mixture into the sauce and gently heat through. When the pasta is al dente, drain and serve topped with the sauce.

ANALYSIS	4		6	
Energy (kJ Cal)	2870	677	1912	457
● Carb (g)		104		69
● Prot (g)		52		35
● Fat (g)		6		4
● Calcium, Iron, Zinc				

HINT. *Use wholemeal pasta if you want to increase your fibre intake. Serve with a salad for an extra vitamin boost or add more vegetables to the sauce to make a complete meal.*

Preparation time: 15 minutes
Cooking time: 15 minutes

fettucine with fresh tomato & chickpeas Serves 4-6

500 g fettucine
spray olive oil
300 g can chickpeas, rinsed and drained
2 tablespoons capers (optional)
1 small red onion, chopped
4 ripe tomatoes, chopped
⅓ cup chopped fresh parsley
1-2 tablespoons lemon juice, to taste
freshly ground black pepper, to taste

Cook the fettucine in a large pan of boiling water until al dente. Drain and return to the pan. Add a spray of olive oil and toss to coat the pasta. Combine the chickpeas, capers, onion, tomatoes and parsley. Season with the lemon juice and black pepper, and serve with the fettucine.

ANALYSIS	4		6	
Energy (kJ Cal)	2235	534	1490	356
● Carb (g)		101		67
● Prot (g)		20		14
● Fat (g)		4		3
● Phyto-chemicals, Vitamin C				
● Fibre, Iron				

HINT: *This dish is best made using ripe, flavoursome tomatoes when they are in season.*

Preparation time: 10 minutes
Cooking time: 10 minutes

fettucine with chicken & lemon Serves 4-6

500 g fettucine
spray of canola or olive oil
500 g or two skinless chicken breast fillets, cut into thin strips
250 mL (1 cup) MAGGI Chicken Stock
60 mL (¼ cup) lemon juice
2 teaspoons finely grated lemon rind
1 cup frozen peas
60 g reduced-fat cream cheese, chopped
freshly ground black pepper, to taste

Start cooking the pasta in a large saucepan of boiling water. Spray a nonstick frying pan with oil and heat. Add the chicken and cook over medium-high heat for about 5 minutes or until browned and cooked through. Remove from the pan, set aside and keep warm. Add the stock, lemon juice, rind and peas to the pan. Bring to the boil, reduce the heat slightly and simmer for 2–3 minutes or until the peas are cooked. Add the cream cheese and stir over low heat until smooth. When the pasta is al dente, drain and return to the pan. Add the sauce and toss to combine. Season with black pepper and serve immediately with the chicken.

ANALYSIS		4	6
	Energy (kJ Cal)	2745 655	1829 437
●	Carb (g)	91	61
●	Prot (g)	46	31
●	Fat (g)	11	8
●	Iron, Zinc		

HINT: *Serve with a salad for a vitamin boost, or add more vegetables to make a complete meal. Use wholemeal pasta if you want to increase your fibre intake.*

Preparation time: 10 minutes
Cooking time: 15 minutes

rigatoni with salmon & ricotta Serves 4-6

500 g rigatoni
2 small salmon fillets (about 300 g)
spray of canola or olive oil
1 small onion, finely chopped
3 stalks celery, finely sliced
2 zucchini (courgette), sliced
200 g low-fat ricotta cheese
2 teaspoons chopped fresh dill
freshly ground black pepper, to taste
lemon juice, to taste

Start cooking the pasta in a large saucepan of boiling water. Meanwhile, place the salmon fillets in a frying pan and cover with cold water. Place over low heat and cover (if you don't have a lid, use a flat baking tray). The water should be just moving on the surface, not boiling or simmering. Cook for about 7 minutes or just until the flesh changes colour. Test by inserting the point of a sharp knife into the thickest part and gently flake the fish. Lift the fish from the pan with a slotted spoon or spatula and drain on paper towels. Spray a nonstick frying pan with oil and heat. Add the onion, celery and zucchini and cook over medium heat, stirring occasionally, for about 3 minutes or until soft. When the pasta is al dente, drain and return to the pan. Gently break the salmon apart with a fork and add to the pasta along with the vegetables. Crumble the ricotta over the pasta and add the dill. Season with pepper and a squeeze of lemon juice. Toss to combine thoroughly, and serve immediately.

ANALYSIS		4	6
	Energy (kJ Cal)	2550 608	1700 405
●	Carb (g)	90	60
●	Prot (g)	32	21
●	Fat (g)	12	8
●	Calcium		
●	Iron, Zinc		

HINT: *You can replace the fresh salmon with a 210 g can of salmon, well drained, but there is no need to cook it — just add it to the pasta with the vegetable mixture.*

Preparation time: 15 minutes
Cooking time: 15 minutes

fettucine with chicken & lemon

" Lots of good healthy recipes also work well for dinner parties. I had some friends over and cooked Louise's lasagne and some garlic bread. Everyone was really impressed by the look and flavour of the meal. I think the lasagne tastes better than restaurant versions. Of course, I didn't give away the secret recipe."

ANGIE KENNEDY ~ swimmer

rigatoni with salmon & ricotta

spirals with pumpkin & pesto

vegetable lasagne

"The biggest challenge that I faced when I moved out from the AIS was thinking of new meal ideas that ensured I was eating everything I needed. It is hard to keep thinking up new menus. Meals need to be very quick and easy as I'm tired after a hard day's training, and the last thing on my mind is cooking dinner." NICK AHERN ~ walker

spirals with pumpkin & pesto Serves 4-6

500 g spiral pasta
1 cup firmly packed fresh basil leaves
2 teaspoons minced garlic
2 tablespoons toasted pine nuts
2 tablespoons finely grated Parmesan cheese
1 tablespoon olive oil
60 mL (¼ cup) MAGGI Chicken or Vegetable Stock
450 g butternut pumpkin, peeled and cut into small cubes
freshly ground black pepper, to taste

Start cooking the pasta in a large saucepan of boiling water. Place the basil, garlic, pine nuts and Parmesan into a food processor and process until finely chopped. With the motor running, gradually add the oil and stock and process until well combined. Steam or microwave the pumpkin cubes until tender. When the pasta is al dente, drain and return to the pan. Add the pesto, stir to coat the pasta, then add the pumpkin and toss through. Season and serve immediately with salad.

ANALYSIS	4	6
Energy (kJ Cal)	2425 580	1379 330
● Carb (g)	97	53
● Prot (g)	20	12
● Fat (g)	12	8
● Phyto-chemicals		

HINT: *Toasted pine nuts add good flavour. Spread nuts on an oven tray and bake in a preheated 180°C (350°F) oven for about 3 minutes.*

Preparation time: 20 minutes
Cooking time: 10 minutes

vegetable lasagne Serves 4-6 ❄

1 onion, finely chopped
2 teaspoons minced garlic
2 zucchini (courgette), grated
400 g sweet potato (kumera), grated
150 g button mushrooms, chopped
825 g can chopped tomatoes
3 tablespoons tomato paste
2 teaspoons sugar
salt and freshly ground black pepper or mixed herbs, to taste
spray of canola or olive oil
375 g fresh lasagne sheets
500 g low-fat ricotta cheese
½ cup grated Parmesan cheese

Preheat the oven to moderate (180°C or 350°F). Spray a large pan with oil and heat. Add the onion and cook over medium heat for 3 minutes or until soft. Add the garlic and cook for 1 minute more. Add the zucchini (courgette), sweet potato (kumera), mushrooms, tomatoes and tomato paste. Bring to the boil, then reduce heat and simmer for 5 minutes. Stir in the sugar, and season to taste. Spray the base of a large lasagne dish lightly with oil. Cut the lasagne sheets to size and arrange a layer of sheets over the base of the dish. Top with a thin layer of sauce, then continue layering pasta and sauce, making one of the layers with the low-fat ricotta. Finish with a thin layer of sauce on top, sprinkle with Parmesan and bake for 30 minutes. Stand for 5 minutes before cutting into squares to serve.

HINT: *Different vegetables may be used in this recipe. Just chop, or finely grate where appropriate, to reduce cooking time.*

ANALYSIS	4	6
Energy (kJ Cal)	2643 630	1762 421
● Carb (g)	79	53
● Prot (g)	35	23
● Fat (g)	19	13
● Calcium, Phyto-chemicals, Vitamin C		

Preparation time: 25 minutes
Cooking time: 30 minutes

spaghetti with creamy ham sauce Serves 4-6

500 g spaghetti
spray of canola or olive oil
1 onion, finely chopped
150 g button mushrooms, quartered
1 teaspoon minced garlic
1 tablespoon cornflour
525 mL (2 cups) CARNATION Light and Creamy Evaporated Milk
200 g lean sliced ham, cut into strips
1 tablespoon chopped fresh parsley
freshly ground black pepper, to taste

Start cooking the pasta in a large saucepan of boiling water. Meanwhile, spray a frying pan or wok with oil and heat. Add the onion and mushrooms and cook over medium heat for 3 minutes or until soft. Add garlic and cook for 1 minute more. Put the cornflour into a small bowl and gradually add 80 mL (1/3 cup) milk, stirring until smooth. Add the remaining milk to the pan then gradually add the cornflour mixture, stirring constantly. Keep stirring until the sauce boils and thickens. Stir in the ham and parsley, season to taste. When the pasta is al dente, drain and return to the saucepan. Add the sauce and toss through the pasta. Serve immediately with salad.

ANALYSIS	4	6
Energy (kJ Cal)	2632 629	1755 419
● Carb (g)	106	71
● Prot (g)	35	23
● Fat (g)	7	4
● Calcium, Zinc		
● Iron		

HINT: *When making a cornflour-based sauce, make sure the cornflour is well combined with the first part of the milk, before adding the rest, to prevent the sauce becoming lumpy.*

Preparation time: 10 minutes
Cooking time: 10 minutes

spaghetti with creamy ham sauce

" I heard about the secret lasagne recipe in 1993, but I had to wait until 1999 to actually try it. It was worth the wait. I would make it again. It's so simple. "

SAMANTHA RILEY ~ swimmer

seafood penne Serves 4-6

500 g penne
spray of canola or olive oil
400 g seafood marinara mix
2 tablespoons chopped fresh parsley
1 onion, finely chopped
2 teaspoons minced garlic
1 teaspoon chopped chilli
825 g can crushed tomatoes
freshly ground black pepper, to taste

Start cooking the pasta in a large saucepan of boiling water. Spray a nonstick frying pan or wok with oil and heat. Cook the seafood in batches over medium-high heat until golden and tender. Toss through the parsley, remove the cooked seafood from the pan and set aside. Spray a clean nonstick frying pan or wok with oil and heat. Cook the onion over medium heat for 3 minutes or until soft. Add the garlic and chilli and cook, stirring, for 1 minute more. Add tomatoes and bring to the boil. Reduce heat slightly and simmer uncovered for 5 minutes. Season with black pepper to taste. When the pasta is al dente, drain and serve topped with the tomato sauce and the seafood. Serve with salad.

ANALYSIS	4	6
Energy (kJ Cal)	2345 560	1562 373
● Carb (g)	96	64
● Prot (g)	33	22
● Fat (g)	4	3
● Iron, Zinc		
● Phyto chemicals		

HINT: *Marinara mix usually contains mussels, calamari, scallops, small octopus and fish pieces, but they do vary. You can also buy frozen marinara mix but remember any unused portion must be discarded. Never refreeze seafood once it thaws.*

Preparation time: 10 minutes
Cooking time: 15 minutes

seafood penne

spirals with mexican-style sauce

mexican chicken lasagne

"Maintaining a low-fat diet assists in keeping my body weight and skinfold at an optimal racing level. Remember I have to carry any extra weight up the hills with me! However, low-fat eating doesn't mean 'no-fat' eating. It means taking a little care in how you cook and how you choose foods. The supermarket contains many hidden surprises. I remember to read the small print on food labels — the words 'pure' and 'fresh' and 'natural' are sometimes used to sell foods that are loaded with fats I don't need." MARY GRIGSON ~ mountain bike rider

spirals with mexican-style sauce Serves 4-6

spray of canola or olive oil
1 onion, finely chopped
2 teaspoons minced garlic
2 teaspoons ground cumin
2 teaspoons ground coriander
1 teaspoon chilli powder
1 red capsicum, chopped
1 green capsicum, chopped
440 g can kidney beans, rinsed and drained
3 large tomatoes, chopped
2 tablespoons tomato paste
500 g spiral pasta
1/4 cup fresh coriander leaves

Spray a large pan with oil and heat. Cook the onion for 3 minutes over medium heat or until soft. Add the garlic, cumin, coriander and chilli and cook, stirring, for 1 minute more. Add the capsicum, beans, tomatoes and tomato paste and bring to the boil. Reduce the heat and simmer, partially covered, for 10 minutes. While the sauce is simmering, cook the pasta in a large pan of boiling water until al dente. Drain well. Stir the coriander into the sauce and serve over the pasta.

ANALYSIS	4	6
Energy (kJ Cal) 2449 585	1633 390	
● Carb (g)	111	74
● Prot (g)	24	16
● Fat (g)	4	3
● Fibre, Phyto-chemicals, Vitamin C		
● Iron, Zinc		

HINT: *Fresh coriander leaves add distinct flavour and should not be confused with ground coriander, made from the seed of the same plant. Top with plain low-fat yogurt for added calcium and protein.*

Preparation time: 15 minutes
Cooking time: 15 minutes

mexican chicken lasagne Serves 4-6 ❄

spray of canola or olive oil
400 g lean minced chicken
1 red capsicum, finely chopped
1 teaspoon finely chopped red chilli
440 g can red kidney beans, rinsed and drained
575 g jar tomato-based pasta sauce
400 g can crushed tomatoes
375 g fresh lasagne sheets
375 g low-fat ricotta cheese
1/2 cup grated reduced-fat cheese

Preheat the oven to moderate (180°C or 350°F). Spray a nonstick frying pan with oil and heat. Cook the mince over high heat for about 5 minutes, or until browned, using a wooden spoon to break up the lumps. Add the capsicum, chilli, beans, pasta sauce and tomatoes and stir to combine. Spray the base of a large lasagne dish lightly with oil. Cut the pasta sheets to size and arrange a layer of pasta over the base of the dish. Top with a thin layer of sauce. Continue layering the pasta and sauce, finishing with a layer of pasta. Spread the ricotta over the pasta, and sprinkle with the grated cheese. Bake for 30 minutes or until the lasagne begins to brown around the edges. Stand for 5 minutes before cutting into squares to serve.

ANALYSIS	4	6
Energy (kJ Cal)	3127 747	2085 498
● Carb (g)	87	58
● Prot (g)	57	38
● Fat (g)	19	13
● Calcium, Iron, Phyto-chemicals		
● Fibre, Zinc		

HINT: *Serve with a large crusty roll to increase the carbohydrate level and with a salad for an added vitamin boost.*

Preparation time: 15 minutes
Cooking time: 40 minutes

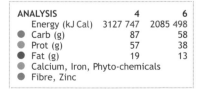

tuna macaroni cheese Serves 4-6

400 g macaroni
spray canola or olive oil
1 small onion, finely chopped
1 stalk celery, finely sliced
440 g can corn kernels, drained
2 tablespoons cornflour
375 mL can CARNATION Light and Creamy Evaporated Milk
125 mL (½ cup) MAGGI Chicken Stock
½ cup grated reduced-fat tasty cheese
440 g can tuna in brine, drained and flaked

Start cooking pasta in a large pan of boiling water. Meanwhile, spray a large pan with oil and heat. Add the onion and celery and cook over medium heat for 3 minutes or until soft. Stir in the corn kernels. Put the cornflour into a small bowl and gradually add 80 mL (⅓ cup) milk, stirring until smooth. Add the remaining milk and the stock to the pan then gradually add the cornflour mixture, stirring constantly. Keep stirring until the sauce boils and thickens. Remove from heat and stir in the cheese until melted. When the pasta is al dente, drain and add with the tuna to the pan. Stir to combine, and serve immediately.

ANALYSIS	4		6	
Energy (kJ Cal)	3085	736	2055	496
● Carb (g)		104		70
● Prot (g)		54		36
● Fat (g)		11		7
● Calcium, Iron, Zinc				

HINT: *You can also garnish this dish with a sprinkle of parsley and lemon rind.*

Preparation time: 15 minutes
Cooking time: 10 minutes

tuna macaroni cheese

" We use teamwork in our household. We swim in different squads and our weekly timetables are always changing, so we have a meeting at the beginning of the week to sort out our individual schedules and assign the duties. We try to alternate who cooks each night. It is good to be able to cover the other person on their busy days and get some help on yours."

MELANIE DODD ~ swimmer

spaghetti bolognese Serves 4-6 ❄ *(sauce only)*

spray of canola or olive oil
1 large onion, chopped
2 teaspoons minced garlic
500 g premium lean beef mince
200 g button mushrooms, thickly sliced
2 teaspoons dried Italian herbs
825 g can crushed tomatoes
2 tablespoons tomato paste
250 mL (1 cup) MAGGI Beef Stock
salt and freshly ground black pepper, to taste
500 g spaghetti

Spray a large pan with oil and heat. Add the onion and cook over medium heat for 3 minutes or until soft. Add the garlic and cook for 1 minute more. Add the beef mince, and cook for about 5 minutes over high heat, or until browned, using a fork to break up the lumps. Add the mushrooms, herbs, tomatoes, tomato paste and stock. Bring to the boil, reduce the heat to low and simmer, uncovered, for 20 minutes, stirring regularly. Season to taste. While the sauce is simmering, cook the pasta in a large saucepan of boiling water until al dente. Drain and serve topped with the sauce. Enjoy with a crispy salad.

HINT: *For a quick, no-fuss bolognese sauce, use 500 g lean minced beef (premium grade is best); 575 g jar tomato-based pasta sauce; 500 g spaghetti; and a tablespoon of grated reduced-fat cheese. Following the above recipe, cook the mince until browned all over, add pasta sauce and stir well. (You can also add 500 g of frozen stirfry-style vegetables for a more balanced meal.) Serve the sauce over pasta with a sprinkle of grated cheese.*

Preparation time: 15 minutes
Cooking time: 30 minutes

ANALYSIS	4		6	
Energy (kJ Cal)	2867	684	1911	457
● Carb (g)		97		65
● Prot (g)		45		30
● Fat (g)		11		7
● Iron, Zinc				

spaghetti bolognese

quick pasta casserole

louise's secret lasagne

"I like to do cooking classes early in the year with a new intake of scholarship athletes. It sets an informal environment where you can get to know the athletes, and get a feel for the nutrition issues they're interested in. It makes nutrition a fun thing. Many athletes have a preconceived view that nutrition is about weight control and being nagged to eat vegetables. It's good to position it in a positive light and provide athletes with skills that will last their whole lives. I love it when you bump into one of the athletes years later and they tell you they're still cooking a certain recipe you taught them." LOUISE BURKE ~ sports dietitian

quick pasta casserole Serves 4-6

spray of canola or olive oil
1 onion, chopped
300 g lean lamb mince
2 zucchini (courgette), thinly sliced
1 carrot, thinly sliced
100 g button mushrooms, thinly sliced
400 g can chopped tomatoes
375 g jar tomato-based pasta sauce
375 g shell pasta, cooked

SAUCE
1½ tablespoons cornflour
375 mL can CARNATION Light and Creamy Evaporated Milk
½ cup grated reduced-fat tasty cheese

Preheat the oven to moderate (180°C or 350°F). Spray a large pan with oil and heat. Add the onion and cook over medium heat for 3 minutes or until soft. Add the mince and cook for about 5 minutes, or until browned, breaking up any lumps with a fork. Add the remaining ingredients, except the pasta. Bring to the boil, reduce the heat and simmer for 5 minutes. Stir in the pasta and transfer to a 2 litre (8 cup) capacity casserole dish. To make the sauce, put the cornflour into a small bowl and gradually add 80 mL (⅓ cup) milk, stirring until smooth. Pour the remaining milk into a small pan, gradually add the cornflour mixture and stir constantly until the sauce boils and thickens. Remove from heat, add half the cheese and stir until melted. Pour the sauce over the pasta mixture and sprinkle with the remaining cheese. Bake for 25 minutes or until golden brown on top.

ANALYSIS	4	6
Energy (kJ Cal)	2770 660	1845 440
● Carb (g)	95	63
● Prot (g)	45	30
● Fat (g)	10	7
● Calcium, Iron, Phyto-chemicals, Zinc		

HINT: *Use wholemeal pasta if you need to increase your fibre intake. Substitute other chopped vegetables as desired.*

Preparation time: 15 minutes
Cooking time: 40 minutes

louise's secret lasagne Serves 4-6 ❋

spray of canola or olive oil
800 g lean beef mince
575 g jar of tomato-based pasta sauce
herbs and spices, to taste
375 g fresh lasagne sheets
450 g can of tomato soup
½ cup grated reduced-fat tasty cheese

Preheat the oven to 170°C (325°F). Spray a nonstick frying pan or wok with oil and heat. Add mince and brown completely. Add pasta sauce and simmer for a few minutes. Season with herbs to taste. Spray the base of a lasagne or casserole dish with oil. Make the lasagne starting with a layer of pasta and alternating with a thin layer of sauce. You should fit 6 layers of pasta in a typical lasagne dish. Finish with a layer of pasta. Pour soup over the assembled lasagne and sprinkle a thin layer of cheese on top. Bake in the oven for 25–30 minutes. Serve with a salad or steamed vegetables and crusty bread.

ANALYSIS	4	6
Energy (kJ Cal)	2841 679	1894 452
● Carb (g)	78	52
● Prot (g)	60	40
● Fat (g)	14	9
● Iron, Zinc		
● Calcium		

HINT: *This recipe can also be made with tuna or salmon, minced chicken or finely chopped vegetables instead of the beef.*

Preparation time: 15 minutes
Cooking time: 40 minutes

spice

spice

Gone are the days when an athlete's diet deserved the reputation for being bland. Today's champions fuel their winning performances with meals that are full of flavour. Stirfries and curries are tasty, quick to prepare and make perfect partners for rice, noodles and other carbohydrate-rich foods. With some practice and a little creativity, an infinite number of tasty stirfries and curries can be produced, combining protein-rich foods and vegetables with flavoursome sauces. To keep these dishes low in fat, choose lean cuts of meat, pork and poultry, and minimise the oil added in cooking.

Although curries have the reputation for being ferocious dishes, not all curries are hot. In fact many are spicy without the slightest sting. In the following recipes, you can adjust the amount of chilli and spices to suit individual tastes.

A key item for cooking these dishes is a good-quality nonstick wok or large frying pan. This allows you to cook quickly over a hot flame or element, and to use the minimum amount of oil. Nonstick surfaces only need a light brush of oil or a coat of spray-on oil. For added flavour, use olive, peanut or sesame oil.

Stirfries need to be cooked quickly so you should have all your ingredients ready before you start cooking. Ingredients are best chopped into bite-size pieces or long thin strips to make sure they cook quickly and evenly.

Make sure the wok is hot before you add the ingredients so that the food cooks fast. If you are cooking a large amount of meat, add one handful at a time then remove the cooked portion and set aside before adding a new batch. Once all the meat is cooked, assemble all the ingredients and seasonings back in the hot wok. You can turn down the heat once the wet ingredients are added so the mixture simmers for the last few minutes.

hints & tips

Timing is essential for stirfries as they are best eaten hot and freshly cooked, and you have to coordinate the cooking of rice, pasta or noodle partners. For rice and dry pastas, start boiling water in a separate saucepan before you begin the stirfry recipe. When the rice or pasta is cooked, rinse, drain through a colander and return to the saucepan to keep warm.

To save time, replace fresh vegetables with frozen stirfry-style vegetables. Stir well in the wok to ensure the frozen vegetables separate and cook evenly.

For well-balanced vegetarian meals, substitute meat with tofu, nutmeat or beans. Tofu is a good substitute for chicken or fish and needs to be added to the dish early with sauce or spices to develop a good flavour. Nutmeat and other meat alternatives can be added later in the cooking process.

Fresh seafood needs to be shelled, cleaned and deveined before cooking. For a quick option, replace individual items with a prepared seafood marinara mix.

Many traditional curries use large amounts of high-fat ingredients such as oil, ghee (clarified butter) or coconut milk or cream, but these can be replaced with reduced-fat or 'light' versions (check the labels for products with 5 g fat per 100 mL or less). You can also make a coconut milk substitute using CARNATION Light and Creamy Evaporated Milk thickened with cornflour. Mix the cornflour with enough milk to form a smooth paste then slowly add the rest of the milk while stirring. Add a few drops of coconut essence for flavour.

Accompaniments for curry can often add extra carbohydrate to the meal. Pappadams are very low in fat and easy to prepare (place on a paper towel and cook in the microwave or oven according to directions). Naan breads are widely available or can be made at home using round flatbread or pita bread. Slice open the pocket and place low-fat yogurt, almonds and sultanas inside. Bake in a preheated 180°C (350°F) oven for 5–10 minutes. Sliced banana sprinkled with lemon juice and a tablespoon of dessicated coconut is another great side dish.

To counteract curry that gets too spicy, add a spoonful of low-fat natural yogurt. It is an excellent remedy for burnt palates and is an added source of calcium.

chicken with mango Serves 4-6

spray canola or olive oil
500 g or two skinless chicken breast fillets, cut into thin strips
1 onion, chopped
450 g butternut pumpkin, cut into 1 cm cubes
1 teaspoon minced garlic
1 teaspoon curry powder
2 tablespoons tomato paste
1 cup light coconut milk
425 mL (1²/₃ cups) apricot nectar
2 tablespoons cornflour
425 g can mango slices, drained
2 cups couscous

Spray a nonstick wok or frying pan with oil and heat. Cook the chicken in 2 or 3 batches over high heat for 2–3 minutes or until browned. Remove from the pan and set aside. Reheat the wok and stirfry the onion and pumpkin for 3 minutes or until soft. Add the garlic, curry powder and tomato paste, stirfry for 30 seconds. Stir in the coconut milk, and about three quarters of the apricot nectar. Bring to the boil, reduce the heat slightly and simmer for about 5 minutes or until the pumpkin is tender. Return the chicken to the pan. Put cornflour in a small bowl and gradually add the remaining nectar, stirring until smooth. Add to pan and stir until the sauce thickens. Stir in mango slices. Put the couscous in a heatproof bowl and add 2 cups of boiling water. Cover tightly, stand for 3 minutes, then fluff up with a fork before serving with the chicken spooned over it.

ANALYSIS		4	6
Energy (kJ Cal)		3045 727	2030 485
● Carb (g)		121	80
● Prot (g)		42	28
● Fat (g)		8	6
● Iron, Phyto-chemicals			

HINT: *Canned mango makes this dish possible year round, but use fresh mango when in season. Add green vegetables to make a complete meal.*

Preparation time: 15 minutes
Total cooking time: 20 minutes

chicken & vegetable stirfry Serves 4-6

250 g dried thin egg noodles
spray canola or olive oil
500 g or two skinless chicken breast fillets, cut into thin strips
2 teaspoons minced ginger
1 teaspoon minced garlic
1 small onion, chopped
1 red and 1 green capsicum, thinly sliced
250 g snow peas, halved
60 mL (¼ cup) plum sauce
2 tablespoons MAGGI Sweet Chilli Sauce
80 mL (⅓ cup) MAGGI Chicken Stock

Cook the noodles in a large pan of boiling water for 5 minutes or until tender. Drain well then toss with a little oil to prevent them sticking. Set aside. Spray a nonstick wok or frying pan with oil and heat. Cook the chicken in 2 or 3 batches over high heat for 2–3 minutes or until browned. Set the cooked chicken aside. Reheat the wok, add the ginger, garlic and the onion and stirfry for 2 minutes or until soft. Add the capsicum and snow peas and stirfry for about 3 minutes or until tender but still crisp. Add the sauces and stock and bring to the boil. Add the noodles and toss to warm through. Return the chicken to the pan and reheat. Serve immediately.

ANALYSIS		4	6
Energy (kJ Cal)		2450 584	1630 390
● Carb (g)		86	57
● Prot (g)		44	30
● Fat (g)		6	4
● Iron, Vitamin C			
● Zinc			

HINT: *This recipe works well using tofu or nutmeat as a vegetarian alternative to chicken.*

Preparation time: 15 minutes
Cooking time: 20 minutes

chicken with mango

" In Germany, we stayed in apartments and it was a good change from hotel living.
It was important to have new recipes to jazz things up.
It's not that the girls can't cook, but it's great to have some fresh ideas that are easy and can be cooked with limited supplies."

JAMES VICTOR ~ coach, women's cycling

chicken & vegetable stirfry

tofu vegetable stirfry

pork & vegetable stirfry

"You have to have a good wok. It's great for whipping up stirfries. One of my favourite dishes is a stirfry chicken with tenderloins, fresh garlic and onion, red chilli peppers and ginger. I use lots of sweet chilli sauce, oyster sauce and soy sauce, and add some bok choy. Cooking up hokkien noodles is really easy — they only take a minute or two to cook. It tastes terrific." SCOTT MILLER ~ swimmer

tofu vegetable stirfry Serves 4-6

900 g Hokkien noodles
2 baby bok choy
spray canola or olive oil
1 onion, sliced into thin wedges
150 g button mushrooms, sliced
1 large carrot, thinly sliced
200 g cauliflower, cut into small florets
200 g broccoli, cut into small florets
1 red capsicum, chopped
200 g firm tofu, cubed
80 mL (⅓ cup) kecap manis, or soy sauce

Place the noodles into a large heatproof bowl and cover with boiling water. Stand for 2 minutes, pushing gently with a wooden spoon to separate the strands. Drain well and set aside. Trim the ends from the bok choy, separate the leaves and cut into wide strips. Spray a large nonstick wok or frying pan with oil. Add the onion, and stirfry for 1 minute or until it starts to soften. Add the vegetables except the bok choy, and stirfry for 3 minutes or until they are tender but still crisp. Add the bok choy, toss through, then the tofu and stir to heat through. Add the noodles, toss to combine and heat through. Add sauce and stir. Serve immediately.

ANALYSIS	4	6
Energy (kJ Cal)	2312 552	1541 368
● Carb (g)	92	61
● Prot (g)	27	18
● Fat (g)	9	6
● Phyto-chemicals, Vitamin C		

HINT: *Kecap manis is an Indonesian soy sauce, quite thick and sweet. It is available in most supermarkets.*

Preparation time: 15 minutes
Cooking time: 10 minutes

pork & vegetable stirfry Serves 4-6

1 bunch asparagus
1 large carrot
2 cups white long-grain rice
spray canola or olive oil
500 g pork fillet, cut into thin strips
1 onion, cut into thin wedges
1 teaspoon minced garlic
2 teaspoons minced ginger
125 mL (½ cup) plum sauce
1 tablespoon soy sauce

Trim the woody ends from asparagus and cut into 4 cm lengths. Peel the carrots and cut into thin sticks about 4 cm long. Cook the rice in a large pan of boiling water for about 12 minutes or until tender. Spray a nonstick wok or frying pan with oil and heat. Stirfry the meat in 2 batches over high heat for 3–4 minutes or until well browned and tender. Remove from the pan and set aside. Add the onion to the pan and stirfry over medium-high heat for 2 minutes or until beginning to soften. Add the garlic, ginger, asparagus and carrot and stirfry for 3 minutes or until vegetables are tender but still crisp. Return meat to the pan along with the plum and soy sauces. Stir to heat through and serve with the rice.

ANALYSIS	4	6
Energy (kJ Cal)	2492 595	1662 397
● Carb (g)	102	68
● Prot (g)	37	25
● Fat (g)	4	3
● Iron, Zinc		
● Phyto-chemicals		

HINT: *You can also serve this dish with 375 g pasta spirals or shells, cooked until al dente, as an alternative to the rice.*

Preparation time: 10 minutes
Cooking time: 15 minutes

beef with cashews Serves 4-6

2 cups long-grain or jasmine rice
spray canola or olive oil
500 g lean beef, cut into thin strips
1 small onion, cut into thin wedges
1 teaspoon minced ginger
1 teaspoon minced garlic
1 red capsicum, cut into thin strips
250 g snow peas, halved
400 g can baby corn
200 g broccoli, cut into florets
2–3 tablespoons kecap manis or soy sauce
125 mL (½ cup) orange juice
100 g roasted cashew nuts

Cook the rice in a large saucepan of boiling water for about 12 minutes or until tender. Drain well. Spray a nonstick wok or large frying pan with oil and heat. Stirfry the meat in 2 batches over high heat for 3-4 minutes or until well browned and tender. Remove from the pan. Reheat the wok, add the onion, ginger and garlic and stirfry for 2 minutes or until soft. Add the remaining vegetables and stirfry for about 3 minutes or until tender but still crisp. Add the kecap manis or soy sauce and juice and stir through. Return beef to the pan and stir for 1 minute or until heated through. Mix in the nuts and serve immediately over the rice.

ANALYSIS		4	6
Energy (kJ Cal)	2795 668	1863 445
● Carb (g)		93	62
● Prot (g)		43	29
● Fat (g)		13	9
● Iron, Vitamin C, Zinc			
● Phyto-chemicals			

HINT: *This recipe can also be served with 375 g pasta spirals, cooked until al dente, instead of rice.*

Preparation time: 15 minutes
Cooking time: 15 minutes

beef with cashews

" After training, you're tired and need to eat quickly. Fast food or takeaway meals from a restaurant sometimes seem the easiest option, and I know how to choose healthy things from the menu. But over a period of time, this becomes expensive. In the end, it's good to know how to cook."

MICHAEL KLIM ~ swimmer

thai chicken curry Serves 4-6

spray canola or olive oil
1 onion, cut into thin wedges
2 tablespoons red curry paste
375 mL (1½ cups) can light coconut milk
125 mL (½ cup) MAGGI Chicken Stock
500 g or two skinless chicken breast fillets, cut into strips
250 g green beans, cut into 3 cm lengths
1 green capsicum, thinly sliced
2 slender eggplant (aubergine), thinly sliced
2 cups white long-grain or jasmine rice
1 tablespoon MAGGI Fish Sauce
1 tablespoon lime juice
2 teaspoons brown sugar
2 tablespoons chopped fresh coriander

Spray a nonstick wok or large frying pan with oil and heat. Add the onion and cook over medium heat for 3 minutes or until soft. Add the curry paste and stirfry for 1 minute. Stir in the coconut milk and stock and bring to the boil. Add the chicken, beans, capsicum and eggplant. Reduce the heat slightly and simmer uncovered for 15 minutes or until the vegetables are tender and the chicken is cooked through. Stir occasionally. Cook the rice in a large saucepan of boiling water for about 12 minutes or until tender. Add the fish sauce, juice, sugar and coriander to the curry, stir through, and serve with the rice.

ANALYSIS		4	6
Energy (kJ Cal)	2540 610	1700 405
● Carb (g)		92	61
● Prot (g)		38	25
● Fat (g)		9	6
● Iron, Zinc			

HINT: *Thai curry pastes come in jars, and usually keep for a few months in the fridge. Red or green pastes may be interchanged in these recipes. You can also replace the eggplant with zucchini (courgette).*

Preparation time: 10 minutes
Cooking time: 20 minutes

thai chicken curry

quick vegetarian curry

moroccan-style beef with couscous

"As an ovo-lacto vegetarian athlete, eating is not just a case of pushing meat aside and doubling up on greens. The nutrients that meat provide in a meal need to be replaced, not just ignored. I pay particular attention to my protein intake. I keep a mental record of how often I eat eggs, low-fat dairy products, legumes or nuts. I often find by replacing chicken with tofu and meat with meat alternatives, many non-vegetarian recipes can be quickly modified into meals that are well balanced."

KATE FAIRWEATHER ~ archer

quick vegetarian curry Serves 4-6

200 g sweet potato (kumera), chopped
200 g potato, chopped
spray canola or olive oil
1 onion, chopped
1 red capsicum, chopped
2 teaspoons minced garlic
1 tablespoon green curry paste
2 cups white long-grain or basmati rice
1½ tablespoons cornflour
two 375 mL cans CARNATION Light and Creamy Evaporated Milk
2 cups broccoli florets
200 g can chickpeas, rinsed and drained
2 teaspoons coconut essence

Steam or microwave the sweet potato (kumera) and potato to partially cook. Spray a large pan with oil and heat. Add the onion and capsicum and cook over medium heat for 3 minutes, or until soft, then add the garlic and curry paste and stirfry for 1 minute. Cook the rice in a large pan of boiling water for 12 minutes or until tender. Put the cornflour in a small bowl and gradually add 80 mL (⅓ cup) milk, stirring until smooth. Add potato, sweet potato, broccoli and remaining milk to the pan. Bring to the boil and simmer for 5 minutes or until vegetables are tender. Add cornflour mixture to the pan and stir until sauce thickens, then stir in chickpeas and coconut essence. Serve over the rice or with rice on the side.

ANALYSIS	4	6
Energy (kJ Cal)	2819 673	1879 449
● Carb (g)	127	85
● Prot (g)	30	20
● Fat (g)	4	3
● Calcium, Phyto-chemicals, Vitamin C		
● Iron		

HINT: *The combination of chickpeas, which are a pulse, and rice or couscous, both grains, form complete proteins, making this a nutritious vegetarian dish.*

Preparation time: 10 minutes
Cooking time: 15 minutes

moroccan-style beef with couscous Serves 4-6

spray of canola or olive oil
500 g lean beef, cut into strips
1 onion, cut into thin wedges
1 teaspoon minced garlic
½ teaspoon finely chopped red chilli
1 teaspoon ground cumin
¼ teaspoon turmeric
400 g can crushed tomatoes
250 mL (1 cup) MAGGI Beef Stock
2 zucchini (courgette), sliced
4 large silverbeet leaves, shredded
½ cup sultanas
2 cups couscous
½ cup toasted slivered almonds

Spray a nonstick wok or frying pan with oil and heat. Stirfry beef in 2 batches over high heat for 3–4 minutes or until well browned. Remove from the pan and set aside. Add onion to the pan and cook over medium heat for 3 minutes or until soft. Add the garlic, chilli and spices and stirfry for about 30 seconds. Stir in the tomatoes and stock, bring to the boil and reduce the heat. Add the zucchini, silverbeet and sultanas, simmer for 5 minutes, stirring occasionally. Put the couscous in a heatproof bowl and add 2 cups of boiling water. Cover tightly and stand for 3 minutes, then fluff up with a fork before serving. Return beef to the pan to heat and serve over couscous, sprinkled with almonds.

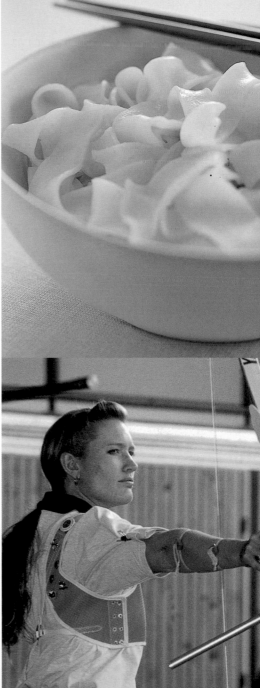

ANALYSIS	4	6
Energy (kJ Cal)	2762 660	1841 440
● Carb (g)	86	58
● Prot (g)	43	29
● Fat (g)	15	11
● Iron, Zinc		
● Phyto-chemicals		

HINT: *This recipe is fairly mild, so add a little more chilli if you like a 'hotter' flavour.*

Preparation time: 20 minutes
Cooking time: 15 minutes

mild beef curry   Serves 4-6   ❄

spray canola or olive oil
750 g lean diced beef
1 large onion, chopped
2 teaspoons minced garlic
2 teaspoons minced ginger
1 tablespoon curry powder
500 mL (2 cups) MAGGI Beef Stock
1 red capsicum, chopped
2 carrots, sliced
500 g potatoes, cut into 3cm pieces

Spray a large pan with oil and heat. Cook the meat over medium heat in 2 batches for 2-3 minutes or until well browned. Set aside. Spray a little more oil into the pan, add the onion and cook for 3 minutes or until soft. Add the garlic, ginger and curry powder and stirfry for about 30 seconds. Gradually add the stock, stirring to scrape the spices from the bottom of the pan. Return the meat to the pan. Bring to the boil, reduce the heat to low and cook, covered, for 30 minutes. Add the vegetables to the pan and cook for a further 30 minutes or until the meat is tender. Uncover the pan for the last 15 minutes of cooking, and stir regularly, so the gravy thickens. Serve with long-grain or basmati rice.

ANALYSIS		4		6
Energy (kJ Cal)	2686	642	1791	428
● Carb (g)		103		69
● Prot (g)		39		26
● Fat (g)		7		5
● Iron, Vitamin C, Zinc				
● Phyto-chemicals				

HINT: *The flavour of curry improves overnight. Transfer to a bowl, cool, cover with plastic wrap and refrigerate until needed. You can also freeze curries in airtight containers.*

Preparation time: 20 minutes
Cooking time: 1 hour

mild beef curry

" Before coming to the AIS, my only cooking experience was to warm up things in a microwave. Now that I've done a couple of cooking classes, I'd even feel confident cooking a romantic dinner for a girl!"

TODD BRODIE ~ soccer player

sweet & sour chicken   Serves 4-6

100 g dried thin egg noodles
spray canola or olive oil
400 g chicken tenderloins, chopped
440 g can pineapple pieces or half a medium-sized pineapple, cut into small wedges
2 teaspoons minced garlic
2 teaspoons minced ginger
250 g button mushrooms, quartered
500 g frozen stirfry vegetable medley (optional)
1 tablespoon cornflour
1 tablespoon soy sauce
3 tablespoons tomato sauce
2 tablespoons vinegar
1 tablespoon brown sugar

Cook the noodles in a large pan of boiling water for 5 minutes or until tender. Drain well and set aside. Spray a nonstick wok or frying pan with oil and heat. Cook chicken in 2 or 3 batches over high heat for 2–3 minutes or until browned. Remove from the pan and set aside. Drain pineapple and reserve the juice. Add garlic and ginger to the pan and stirfry for 30 seconds. Add the mushrooms (and vegetables if desired) and stirfry for 3 minutes or until tender. Put cornflour into a small bowl and gradually add 60 mL (¼ cup) reserved juice, stirring until smooth. Add pineapple, remaining juice, sauces, vinegar and sugar to the pan and bring to the boil. Stir in cornflour mixture and simmer for 2–3 minutes or until the sauce has thickened slightly. Return the chicken to the pan with the noodles and toss until heated through. Garnish with green leafy herbs.

ANALYSIS		4		6
Energy (kJ Cal)	2550	610	1700	405
● Carb (g)		96		64
● Prot (g)		41		28
● Fat (g)		5		4
● Iron				

HINT: *Tenderloins may be replaced with the equal weight of breast fillet. The optional vegetables will make this meal complete.*

Preparation time: 10 minutes
Cooking time: 20 minutes

sweet & sour chicken

seafood & basil stirfry

fish curry

"Being prepared helps you to be able to eat quickly and replace fuel after those long and late training sessions. I half prepare meals before going to training — like browning the chicken and cutting the vegetables for a stirfry or cooking a bolognese sauce. Then when I get home I put on a CD to make me feel relaxed, and complete the meal. Even though it takes a bit of effort, I like cooking. It's simple when you are organised and prepare in advance. I even find it therapeutic."

DAN KOWALSKI ~ swimmer

seafood & basil stirfry   Serves 4-6

2 cups white long-grain or jasmine rice
250 g green (raw) king prawns
400 g white fish fillets
100 g cleaned calamari
spray canola or olive oil
100 g scallops, without roe
2 teaspoons minced garlic
2 teaspoons chopped red chilli
1 red capsicum, sliced
8 spring onions, sliced
2 tablespoons MAGGI Oyster Sauce
2 tablespoons MAGGI Fish Sauce
2 tablespoons water
1/3 cup shredded fresh basil leaves

Cook the rice in a large pan of boiling water for 12 minutes or until tender. Drain well. Peel and devein the prawns, leaving the tails intact. Cut the fish into bite-size pieces. Cut the calamari into small squares and score the inside surface with a sharp knife. Spray a nonstick wok or frying pan with oil and heat. Stirfry the prawns over high heat for 2 minutes or until the flesh becomes opaque. Set aside. Reheat the wok and cook the fish in the same way, remove and set aside. Then stirfry the calamari and scallops together and remove and set aside. Add the garlic and chilli to the pan, stirfry for a few seconds, then add the capsicum and spring onions and stirfry for 2–3 minutes. Add the sauces and the water and bring to the boil. Return all the seafood to the pan along with the basil and quickly toss to heat. Serve immediately over the rice and enjoy with salad.

ANALYSIS		4	6
	Energy (kJ Cal)	2515 601	1676 400
●	Carb (g)	87	58
●	Prot (g)	49	33
●	Fat (g)	6	4
●	Vitamin C, Zinc		
●	Iron		

HINT: *Any of the seafood elements could be increased, decreased or omitted to your liking, but keep the total weight in mind to yield enough for 4–6 servings.*

Preparation time: 15 minutes
Cooking time: 15 minutes

fish curry   Serves 4–6

2 cups white long-grain or basmati rice
600 g firm boneless fish fillets
spray canola or olive oil
1/3 cup curry paste (such as balti or tikka masala)
575 g jar tomato-based pasta sauce
125 mL (1/2 cup) water
500 g frozen stirfry vegetable medley (optional)
125 mL (1/2 cup) low-fat natural yogurt
2 tablespoons finely chopped fresh coriander leaves

Cook the rice in a large pan of boiling water for 12 minutes or until tender. Cut the fish into large bite-size pieces. Spray a nonstick wok or large frying pan with oil and heat, add the curry paste and stirfry over medium heat for 1 minute. Stir in the pasta sauce and water and bring to the boil. Add the fish pieces (and vegetables if desired), reduce the heat slightly and simmer for about 5 minutes or until the fish is cooked (test by flaking the flesh with a fork). Push the fish to one side of the pan and stir the yogurt and coriander into the sauce, then gently stir in the fish to coat. (Stirring the fish too much could cause it to fall apart.) Don't let the sauce boil again after adding the yogurt. Serve with white long-grain or basmati rice.

ANALYSIS		4	6
	Energy (kJ Cal)	2658 635	1772 423
●	Carb (g)	97	65
●	Prot (g)	42	28
●	Fat (g)	8	5
●	Iron		
●	Zinc		

HINT: *Ling, ocean perch or jewfish are suitable types of fish for this recipe. The optional vegetables will make this meal complete.*

Preparation time: 10 minutes
Cooking time: 10 minutes

fruity chicken curry   Serves 4-6   ❄

spray canola or olive oil
1 onion, chopped
1 teaspoon minced garlic
1 tablespoon curry powder
825 g can crushed tomatoes
125 mL (½ cup) MAGGI Chicken Stock
½ cup fruit chutney
500 g or two skinless chicken breast fillets, cut into thin strips
400 g sweet potato (kumera), cut into small cubes
2 cups white long-grain or basmati rice
4 tablespoons low-fat natural yogurt, to serve

Spray a large pan with oil and heat. Cook onion over medium heat for 3 minutes or until soft. Add garlic and curry powder and cook, stirring, for about 30 seconds. Add the remaining ingredients (except the yogurt and rice) and bring to the boil. Reduce heat and simmer, partially covered, for about 20 minutes or until sweet potato is tender. Meanwhile, cook the rice in a large pan of boiling water for 12 minutes or until tender. Serve the curry over the rice, topped with a dollop of yogurt.

fruity chicken curry

ANALYSIS	4	6
Energy (kJ Cal)	2923 698	1959 466
● Carb (g)	120	80
● Prot (g)	40	27
● Fat (g)	6	4
● Iron, Phyto-chemicals, Vitamin C, Zinc		

HINT: *You can also serve this dish with couscous as an alternative to rice (see Chicken with Mango recipe for instructions).*

Preparation time: 10 minutes
Cooking time: 25 minutes

sesame beef   Serves 4-6

2 teaspoons minced garlic
3 tablespoons soy sauce
3 tablespoons MAGGI Oyster Sauce
2 tablespoons lemon juice
2 tablespoons orange juice
500 g lean rump steak, cut into thin strips
900 g Hokkien noodles
spray canola or olive oil
2 carrots, sliced
1 green capsicum, sliced
1 bunch English spinach, trimmed
3 tablespoons toasted sesame seeds
60 g snow pea sprouts

Combine the garlic, soy sauce, oyster sauce and juice in a glass or ceramic dish. Add the beef and toss to coat. Cover and marinate for 15 minutes. Drain the meat and reserve the marinade. Put the hokkien noodles into a large heatproof bowl and cover with boiling water. Leave to stand for 2 minutes, pushing gently with a wooden spoon to separate the strands. Drain well and set aside. Spray a nonstick wok or frying pan with oil and heat. Stirfry the meat in 2 or 3 batches over high heat for 2–3 minutes or until browned. Set aside. Reheat the wok, add the carrots and capsicum and stirfry for 3 minutes, then add the reserved marinade and bring to the boil. Add the spinach leaves and toss until just wilted. Stir in the noodles, beef, sesame seeds and snow pea sprouts, and toss to heat through.

ANALYSIS	4	6
Energy (kJ Cal)	2883 689	1922 459
● Carb (g)	92	61
● Prot (g)	50	33
● Fat (g)	13	9
● Iron, Vitamin C, Zinc		
● Phyto-chemicals		

HINT: *Exchange the various types of noodles, pasta, rice or couscous served with stirfries and curries. Some of the recipes also make delicious fillings for baked potatoes — a great way of using leftovers.*

Preparation time: 15 minutes + marinating
Cooking time: 15 minutes

" Cooking nights are an excellent way for the players to practically apply the principles learnt at nutrition education sessions. The sessions also reinforce good eating habits. Many of the players were surprised at how simple the recipes were to make and in such a short time — and they even tasted good."

ANDY CLARK ~ rugby coach

sesame beef

bakes&
grills

bakes & grills

Traditional dining in Australia often focused on the meat part of a meal, with generous serves taking up most of the plate. This is especially true of roast dinners, grills and barbecues. The good news is that these types of meals don't have to be high in fat or loaded with meat. Our baking, grilling and barbecuing recipes focus on low-fat meals, reducing the amount of meat per serve and finding a carbohydrate partner to ensure that fuelling up is tasty, too.

Bread is a widely available carbohydrate food. If you're stuck at a barbecue or a family dinner with no choice about the menu, you can always balance your meal by enjoying a good serve of bread, plenty of vegetables or salad, and half the usual serve of meat, fish or chicken. If it's one of those occasions where you might take something along, include lots of fresh bread to ensure you can meet your nutritional needs.

Explore the wide range of bread available. Try multigrain and specialty bread, vegetable or fruit loaves, flat bread, plaits and bread sticks, bagels and foccacia. With such a wide variety, it's easy to shift the focus of a meal to delicious bread.

beef & capsicum kebabs Serves 4

MARINADE
2 teaspoons minced garlic
2 tablespoons MAGGI Sweet Chilli Sauce
2 tablespoons soy sauce

500 g rump steak, cut into cubes
1 small red capsicum
1 small green capsicum
16 cherry tomatoes
8 button mushrooms, halved
1 small red onion, cut into wedges

Combine the marinade ingredients in a ceramic or glass bowl. Add the beef and turn to coat thoroughly. Cover and leave for 30 minutes or up to 24 hours. Place the meat in the fridge if marinating for longer than 30 minutes or during very hot weather. Cut the capsicum into small squares. Thread the beef on to the skewers, alternating with the vegetables. Preheat a grill or barbecue grill plate to moderately hot, and cook the skewers for 6 minutes, turning once halfway through. Serve immediately.

ANALYSIS	4
Energy (kJ Cal)	943 225
Carb (g)	9
● Prot (g)	37
● Fat (g)	4
● Iron, Vitamin C, Zinc	

HINT: *A good carbohydrate partner for this meal is rice. Alternatively, remove the skewers and wrap each kebab in a roll or pita bread.*

Preparation time: 20 minutes + marinating
Cooking time: 6 minutes

beef & capsicum kebabs

" I always feel a cooking session has been successful when several athletes say they have cooked a particular dish many times for their friends. Real success is when a rugby player has cooked the dish for his mum (and washed up)!"

NIKKI CUMMINGS ~ sports dietitian

tandoori chicken skewers Serves 4-6

1½ cups long-grain or basmati rice
750 g chicken tenderloins
200 g low-fat natural yogurt
2 teaspoons minced garlic
1 tablespoon tandoori mix
2 tomatoes, finely chopped
1 Lebanese cucumber, finely chopped
1 small red onion, finely chopped
2 tablespoons lemon juice

Cook the rice in a large saucepan of boiling water for about 12 minutes or until tender. Drain well. Meanwhile, cut each tenderloin into pieces, and thread on the skewers. Stir together the yogurt, garlic and tandoori mix until well combined then spoon or brush the mixture over the chicken. Preheat a grill or barbecue grill plate to moderately hot, and cook the skewers for 10 minutes, turning once halfway through. Combine the rice, tomato, cucumber, onion and lemon juice, and serve with the skewers.

ANALYSIS	4	6
Energy (kJ Cal)	2200 525	1466 351
● Carb (g)	66	44
● Prot (g)	52	34
● Fat (g)	5	3
● Iron, Zinc		

HINT: *Add a salad for vitamins and serve with a potato or bread to increase the carbohydrate content.*

Preparation time: 15 minutes
Cooking time: 10 minutes

tandoori chicken skewers

fish in foil parcels

hamburgers

"Since I moved out on my own, I've really gotten into healthy eating. After all, if I was going to give it a go, I wanted to do it right. I've really cut back on takeaways. It helps to do a big shop and have the fridge and cupboards full. Once you've spent the money on good food, you are committed to cooking healthy meals. It has made a huge difference in keeping my skinfolds down. And I feel that I recover more quickly from training sessions." GEOFF HUEGILL ~ swimmer

fish in foil parcels Serves 2

spray of canola or olive oil
4 white boneless fish fillets
2 tablespoons lemon juice
2 spring onions, finely sliced
1 carrot, cut into thin strips
1 zucchini (courgette), cut into thin strips
2 teaspoons finely grated lemon rind

Preheat a barbecue grill plate or frying pan to hot. Tear 4 large square sheets of foil and spray very lightly with oil. Place a fish fillet on each sheet and sprinkle with lemon juice. Divide the spring onions, carrot, zucchini and lemon rind into four portions, and spread over the fish. Fold the foil over to seal completely. Place on the barbecue or in the pan and cook for about 8 minutes. Test the fish by flaking the thickest part of the fillet with a fork – if the flesh is white, the fish is cooked. Serve the fish with rice or boiled new potatoes.

ANALYSIS	2
Energy (kJ Cal)	810 193
Carb (g)	4
● Prot (g)	29
● Fat (g)	6
● Vitamin C	
● Phyto-chemicals	

HINT: *This dish is low in carbohydrates so serve with plenty of rice or potatoes and a large bread roll to reach a carbohydrate 'gold'.*

Preparation time: 10 minutes
Cooking time: 8 minutes

hamburgers Serves 4

BURGERS
500 g premium lean beef mince
1 egg, lightly beaten
1 cup fresh breadcrumbs
1 teaspoon dried mixed herbs
freshly ground black pepper, to taste

4 hamburger rolls, split in half
1 small carrot
4 large lettuce leaves, halved
8 slices beetroot
8 slices tomato
mustard or tomato sauce, to serve

Place the mince, egg, breadcrumbs and herbs into a bowl. Add pepper to taste. Using your hands, mix until well combined, divide into four equal portions and shape each into a patty. Cook patties in a nonstick frying pan or on a barbecue grill plate over medium heat for about 5 minutes on each side or until cooked through. Toast the cut sides of the hamburger buns either on the hot surface of a pan or grill plate, or under a grill. Peel strips from the carrot with a peeler. Place some lettuce on the bottom half of the buns. Top with meat patties, then the beetroot, tomato, carrot and more lettuce. Add mustard or tomato sauce and put on the tops of the buns. Serve immediately.

ANALYSIS	4
Energy (kJ Cal)	2216 529
● Carb (g)	65
● Prot (g)	43
● Fat (g)	11
● Iron, Zinc	
● Phyto-chemicals	

HINT: *Serve with a baked potato to boost the carbohydrate level. Wholemeal bread rolls will provide extra fibre.*

Preparation time: 20 minutes
Cooking time: 10 minutes

potatoes

Where vegetables are mostly valued for vitamins, minerals and fibre, potatoes (and sweet potatoes) are also a good source of carbohydrate. Most athletes think of potatoes as an accompaniment to a meal, favoured in forms such as fries, roast potatoes or mash. Yet all of these side dishes can add a lot of fat to a meal, and what's more, the servings usually don't meet an athlete's requirements for fuel. Here are some easy ways to make the most of potatoes, and turn them into the major fuel source at meals.

Mashed Potatoes / Once the potatoes are cooked and drained, mash them with skim milk. You can also add a small amount of skim milk powder to make them creamier. For other variations, cook sweet potato (kumera), pumpkin, and even carrot with the potatoes and mash together. Fresh herbs such as dill, mint or basil added to the cooked mash also increase the flavour.

Roast Potatoes / Lightly spray the potatoes (or sweet potatoes) with canola oil and place on a large nonstick roasting pan (or a regular pan lined with baking paper). Bake for 45 minutes in a preheated moderately hot oven (200°C or 400°F). When cooked, the potatoes will look golden brown. You can reduce roasting time by partially cooking the potatoes in a microwave for 2–3 minutes per potato before spraying them with the oil and baking.

Homemade Potato Chips / Make homemade potato chips by simply varying the roast potato recipe. Cut the potato into chip-size pieces and place in a microwave-proof bag. Cook the potato in the microwave for 3–5 minutes until softened. Spray an oven tray with olive or canola oil. Remove chips from the bag, place on the tray and spray oil over the chips. Bake in the oven, turning the chips so they cook evenly.

hints & tips

➤ Commercially prepared oven fries are now available in 97 per cent fat-free forms which are acceptably low in fat to provide a good accompaniment to meals. The best types are the thick-cut chips as these absorb less oil per gram than the matchstick-style fries.

➤ For baked potatoes, choose scrubbed or cleaned potatoes so you don't have to remove the skins.

➤ To reduce the cooking time of baked potatoes, partially cook them in the micro-wave (2–3 minutes per medium potato or 5 minutes per large potato) before placing them in the oven. It reduces the total baking time, and the potatoes get a golden brown finish.

➤ Serve baked potato as a meal base instead of rice, pasta and other grains. Try it with some of the recipes in this book such as curries, stirfries and pasta sauces.

➤ For a really easy meal, fill baked potatoes with baked beans and a sprinkle of reduced-fat cheese and then microwave them.

"The hardest part is coming home and being patient while the meal is cooking. It's tempting to fill up on stuff that's lying around in front of you. It works better if you get organised before training and start getting on track for your meal. It's so much better than having to start from scratch when you walk in the door."

SARAH RYAN ~ swimmer

For each of the following baked potato fillings, you will need 4 large evenly shaped potatoes about 300 g each. Clean them if necessary and pat the skin dry with paper towel. Pierce the potatoes a few times with a small sharp knife and place directly on the shelf of a preheated hot (210°C or 415°F) oven and bake for at least 1 hour. Leave in the oven for 1½ hours for really crispy skins. When the potatoes are cooked, cut a cross in the top of each one, pull apart, and spoon heated sauce, casserole or curry over the top.

salmon mornay potato   Serves 2-4

Put 2 teaspoons cornflour into a small bowl and gradually add 60 mL (¼ cup) CARNATION Light and Creamy Evaporated Milk. Stir until smooth. Put 185 mL (¾ cup) milk into a small pan and heat until almost boiling. Add cornflour mix and stir over medium heat until sauce thickens. Stir in ½ cup grated low-fat cheese, 210 g can salmon (well drained) and 1 tablespoon chopped parsley. To serve, open out potatoes and pour the mornay over them.

ANALYSIS		2		4
Energy (kJ Cal)	3614	863	1807	432
● Carb (g)		104		52
● Prot (g)		63		31
● Fat (g)		22		11
● Calcium, Iron, Vitamin C, Zinc				

bean & avocado potato   Serves 2-4

Rinse and drain the contents of a 290 g can red kidney beans. Place in a small saucepan with 200 g jar taco sauce. Stir over medium heat until warmed through. Cut cooked potatoes in half and scoop out flesh. Put into a bowl and mash with half an avocado then return to the potato skins. Spoon the bean mixture over the top, and serve immediately. If desired, sprinkle with a small amount of finely grated low-fat tasty cheese.

ANALYSIS		2		4
Energy (kJ Cal)	3325	794	1663	397
● Carb (g)		125		63
● Prot (g)		29		15
● Fat (g)		19		9
● Fibre, Vitamin C				
● Iron, Phyto-chemicals				

chicken & corn potato   Serves 2-4

Combine 1 cup finely shredded cabbage, 1 small grated carrot and 1 finely sliced spring onion with 1½ tablespoons of low-fat coleslaw dressing. Warm the contents of 130 g can creamed corn in the microwave or on the stove in a small saucepan. Open out the cooked potatoes and spoon the corn over them. Divide 1 cup of sliced or shredded chicken (from a pre-cooked barbecue chicken, or pan-fry a small breast fillet yourself) between the potatoes. Top with the coleslaw, and serve.

ANALYSIS		2		4
Energy (kJ Cal)	2718	649	1359	325
● Carb (g)		103		51
● Prot (g)		41		21
● Fat (g)		7		4
● Iron, Vitamin C, Zinc				
● Fibre, Phyto-chemicals				

curried beef potato   Serves 2-4

Spray a nonstick frying pan with oil and heat. Cook 1 finely chopped small onion over medium heat for 2 minutes or until just soft. Add 200 g lean beef mince and cook for 5 minutes or until browned, breaking up lumps with a wooden spoon. Stir in 2 teaspoons curry powder, finely chopped tomato, 1 grated zucchini and 1 tablespoon tomato paste. Cook, stirring, for another 3 minutes. Spoon the meat over the potatoes and top with a dollop of low-fat natural yogurt.

ANALYSIS		2		4
Energy (kJ Cal)	2652	633	1326	317
● Carb (g)		93		46
● Prot (g)		41		21
● Fat (g)		10		5
● Iron, Vitamin C, Zinc				
● Fibre				

bean & avocado potato

salmon mornay potato

curried beef potato

chicken & corn potato

pizza

Pizza is one of the favourite foods of athletes — we know how often the delivery van comes to the AIS residence. But commercial pizzas can be high in fat if the toppings include fatty meats, thick layers of cheese and stuffed crusts. In your own kitchen you can make pizzas with many gourmet toppings which are based on lean ingredients. Experiment with flavours from a variety of cuisine styles, and try adding fruit and vegetables for colour and additional nutrients.

Pizza bases are widely available in supermarkets. There are many varieties which include:

■ Ready-made bases with tomato topping, found in the fresh produce section of supermarkets.

■ Frozen plain bases which you spread with tomato paste or ready-made pizza sauces.

■ Foccacia bread, round Lebanese bread or pita bread which can be topped with tomato paste or pizza sauce.

■ English muffins or crumpets which also make excellent individual pizzas.

hints & tips

➤ Go for a thick-crust pizza base or bread base. This increases the carbohydrate content of the pizza and gives you a firmer base to pile on the yummy toppings.

➤ Use reduced-fat cheeses — tasty cheese mixed with mozzarella cheese gives a nice finish. But remember these are still quite high in fat so use a sprinkle rather than a full cover. Alternatively, you can use cottage cheese with a final sprinkle of tasty cheese. Pizzas that are well constructed with a variety of toppings, spices and herbs won't miss the thick cheese layer.

➤ The carbohydrate content of pizza can be increased by adding beans (e.g. a Mexican-style pizza) or fruit such as pineapple or banana.

➤ For variety, try different sauce toppings such as pesto, satay, barbecue or chilli.

➤ Pizzas are great for using up leftovers. Almost anything goes as a topping: try tinned tuna, cooked pumpkin, tinned spaghetti or baked beans, grated vegetables, or canned vegetables such as creamed corn or corn kernels. You can also use leftovers from many of our recipes (try stirfries, curries or pasta sauce) as gourmet pizza toppings. Just avoid runny sauces or very wet toppings as they will make the pizza base soggy.

" It's impossible to cook when you come home from training and there's nothing in the cupboard. Getting into a routine is important. I share the tasks like shopping with my housemates. That's the best way when you've got limited time and a busy life."

SAMANTHA RILEY ~ swimmer

To bake the pizza, preheat the oven to moderately hot (200°C or 400°F). When the pizza is ready for baking, place it on an oven tray (you can slide it directly onto the oven shelf but it can be difficult to remove when cooked). Pizzas with a thin crust, such as pita bread, will cook more quickly and may only take 15-20 minutes in the oven. The following toppings are enough for one 30 cm round pizza base or four 15 cm individual bases. If the bases have their own sauce, omit any extra pizza sauce from the recipe.

ham & pineapple pizza Serves 2-4

Spread $1/3$ cup pizza sauce on a base, leaving a 2 cm gap around the edge. Finely chop 1 onion and 1 green capsicum and chop 150 g lean sliced ham. Drain 130 g can corn kernels and 225 g can pineapple pieces. Sprinkle the toppings evenly over the base and top with $1/2$ cup grated low-fat mozzarella cheese. Bake for 30 minutes or until the base is crisp and the cheese melted.

ANALYSIS		2		4
Energy (kJ Cal)	4520	1080	2260	540
● Carb (g)		165		83
● Prot (g)		53		27
● Fat (g)		22		11
● Vitamin C				
● Calcium, Phyto-chemicals, Zinc				

feta & sweet potato pizza Serves 2-4

Spread $1/3$ cup pizza sauce on a base, leaving a 2 cm gap around the edge. Cut very thin slices from 100 g peeled sweet potato (kumera), cut a red capsicum into thin strips and finely slice a small red onion. Arrange the vegetables on the base, then crumble 80 g feta cheese over the top. Bake for 30 minutes or until the base is crisp and the cheese lightly browned. Sprinkle with chopped parsley.

ANALYSIS		2		4
Energy (kJ Cal)	3325	794	1662	397
● Carb (g)		128		64
● Prot (g)		35		17
● Fat (g)		14		7
● Vitamin C				
● Phyto-chemicals				

mexican pizza Serves 2-4

Spray a nonstick pan with oil and heat. Cook a finely chopped small onion over medium heat for 2 minutes or until soft. Add 1 teaspoon chilli powder and cook for 1 minute. Add 200 g lean beef mince and cook for 5 minutes or until browned, breaking up the lumps with a wooden spoon. Turn up the heat to evaporate any liquid, then turn down to low and stir in 200 g jar taco sauce and 290 g can red kidney beans (rinsed and drained). Cool topping slightly and spread on pizza base, leaving a 2 cm gap around the edge. Sprinkle with $1/2$ cup grated low-fat mozzarella cheese and half a green capsicum, chopped. Bake for 30 minutes or until base is crisp and cheese melted. Arrange slices of avocado on top, then cut into wedges to serve.

ANALYSIS		2		4
Energy (kJ Cal)	5065	1210	2532	605
● Carb (g)		145		72
● Prot (g)		66		33
● Fat (g)		36		18
● Calcium, Iron, Zinc				
● Fibre, Phyto chemicals				

seafood pizza Serves 2-4

Spread $1/3$ cup pizza sauce over the base, leaving a 2 cm wide gap around the edge. Scatter a finely sliced red onion and a finely sliced small green capsicum over the base, and top with 100 g peeled prawns, 100 g scallop meat, and 150 g mussel meat. Sprinkle with $1/2$ cup grated low-fat mozzarella cheese, and bake for 30 minutes or until the base is crisp and the cheese melted. Top with chopped parsley.

HINT: *You can also use 350 g of prepared marinara mix purchased from the supermarket or fish market to replace the individual seafood ingredients.*

ANALYSIS		2		4
Energy (kJ Cal)	3587	857	1794	428
● Carb (g)		110		55
● Prot (g)		62		31
● Fat (g)		17		9
● Calcium, Iron, Vitamin C, Zinc				

feta & sweet potato pizza

ham & pineapple pizza

seafood pizza

mexican pizza

treats

treats

At about 2 metres tall and around 16 years of age, the AIS basketball boys take a lot of filling. They depend on snacks and desserts to get all the carbohydrates and kilojoules they need. The girls gymnastic team love their sweets as well but their needs are very different. Their snacks and sweet choices must contain essential nutrients such as calcium, but they don't necessarily need extra kilojoules. The AIS has a variety of sweets and snack recipes to meet the demands of all athletes.

Traditional sweet favourites are often high-fat traps. Donuts, pastries, ice cream and chocolate are all examples of sweets packed with carbohydrate, but also laden with fat. For athletes, there are many lower-fat snack and sweet choices which are high in carbohydrate, nutrient-rich and great tasting. But be wary of high-fat snacks masquerading as healthy options. The amount of fat in some of the so-called health-food muffins, carrot cakes and banana cakes would amaze you.

A sweet treat does not have to be something you spend hours preparing. There are now many commercial alternatives for instant sweet fixes such as tinned or jellied fruit, rice puddings and frozen fruit desserts, and the low-fat versions of yogurt, mousses, ready-made custard and ice cream.

Packet mixes for muffins, puddings, pancakes and cakes are useful time-savers, but check the label for varieties with a low-fat content. Using half the amount of oil or margarine stated in the instructions will keep the fat content low.

Pancake mixes are excellent options as you only need to add water or low-fat milk (as directed) and then shake. Use a nonstick pan and a small amount of oil (or a spray of oil) to keep the added fat as low as possible. Serve these with tinned or fresh fruit for a really quick dessert or snack.

apple & cinnamon muffins   Serves 12   ❄

1½ cups self-raising flour
1 cup wholemeal self-raising flour
2 teaspoons cinnamon
¾ cup brown sugar
¾ cup sultanas
2 apples, peeled and grated
2 tablespoons margarine, melted
310 mL (1¼ cups) skim milk
1 egg, lightly beaten
1 teaspoon vanilla essence

Preheat the oven to moderate (180°C or 350°F). Lightly grease a 12 hole nonstick muffin pan. Sift flours and cinnamon into a large bowl (tip husks from the flour into the bowl, too). Stir in brown sugar, sultanas and grated apple. Make a well in the centre of the mixture. Whisk the margarine, milk, egg and vanilla together with a fork, then add to the flour mixture. Stir gently until the mixture is just combined; don't overbeat or the muffins will be tough. Spoon mixture into the prepared pan. Bake for 20 minutes or until muffins are well risen and spring back to the touch. Leave in the pan for a few minutes then lift out onto a wire rack to cool, or eat while still warm.

HINT: *The muffin mixture only needs to be briefly combined — it may appear a little lumpy but this is normal. Overworking the mixture (for any flour-based product, including cakes and puddings) will make the end product tough. Even nonstick muffin tins will still need to be lightly greased with spray-on oil (especially important for muffins containing ingredients which can stick such as sugar, chocolate or blueberries). Don't leave muffins in the tins too long after baking — they need a few minutes to firm up, but taking them out too soon can also result in them breaking. To remove, run a knife around each muffin then gently prise from the tin.*

ANALYSIS	12
Energy (kJ Cal)	839 200
● Carb (g)	41
Prot (g)	5
● Fat (g)	2

Preparation time: 15 minutes
Cooking time: 20 minutes

blueberry

Leave out cinnamon, sultanas and apple. Replace brown sugar with caster (superfine) sugar. After making the batter, stir in 1 cup fresh or frozen blueberries (no need to thaw), taking care not to overwork the mixture, especially if using frozen berries as the juice will make the muffins purple.

choc-chip

Leave out cinnamon, sultanas and apple. Replace wholemeal flour with white self-raising flour. Replace brown sugar with caster (superfine) sugar. Add 1 cup NESTLÉ Dark CHOC BITS to dry ingredients before stirring in the liquids.

carrot

Replace cinnamon with mixed spice. Replace apple with 1½ cups grated carrot, and replace margarine with 2 tablespoons vegetable oil. Add 1 tablespoon golden syrup to liquid ingredients.

HINT: *Muffin sized paper cases are available in the baking section of most supermarkets. Using them saves on greasing the tins and on washing them up afterwards.*

" Early each year, the AIS Netball Team have a bonding weekend by the beach. A big part of the weekend is sharing the preparation and cooking of meals. You soon find out who knows one end of the saucepan from the other. For a lot of these young athletes, it is their first real experience in preparing meals that will help them perform at the highest level."

LISA BEEHAG ~ netball coach

carrot muffin

apple & cinnamon muffin

choc-chip muffin

blueberry muffin

baked rice custard Serves 4-6

1/3 cup white rice
185 mL (3/4 cup) CARNATION Skim Sweetened Condensed Milk
440 mL (1 3/4 cups) water
3 eggs, lightly beaten
1/4 cup sultanas
nutmeg

Cook rice in a large saucepan of boiling water for about 10 minutes or until tender, and drain well. Preheat the oven to moderate (180°C or 350°F). Stir together milk, water, eggs, rice and sultanas. Pour into a 1 1/4 litre (5 cup) shallow ovenproof baking dish and sprinkle with nutmeg. Stand the dish in a baking pan with enough hot water to reach halfway up the side of the dish. Bake in the oven for 40–45 minutes or until set. Serve hot.

ANALYSIS		4		6
Energy (kJ Cal)	1326	317	884	211
● Carb (g)		60		40
● Prot (g)		12		8
● Fat (g)		4		3
● Calcium				

HINT: *To make a Creamed Rice Pudding based on this recipe, stir 1 cup white rice, 1 litre (4 cups) skim milk, 1/2 cup sugar, 1 teaspoon vanilla essence and 1/2 teaspoon cinnamon in a saucepan over medium heat until thickened and rice is soft. Serve with canned fruit in natural juice.*

Preparation time: 15 minutes
Cooking time: 45 minutes

baked rice custard

" I like the gymnasts to do cooking classes when they come to camp at the AIS because it is a release from the rigours of training. It teaches them practical skills that they will use in the future. The one thing that I would like them to get from their gymnastics career is a healthy attitude to food that will last the rest of their lives."

PEGGY LIDDICK ~ gymnastics coach

berry mousse Serves 4

300 g fresh or frozen raspberries, thawed
two 200 g cartons low-fat strawberry yogurt
1/4 cup icing sugar
2 tablespoons hot water
3 teaspoons gelatine
2 egg whites

Crush raspberries lightly with a fork and combine in a mixing bowl with yogurt and sifted icing sugar. Put the water into a small bowl and sprinkle gelatine over it. Stand the bowl in another bowl of very hot water, and let the gelatine soften for a few minutes then whisk with a fork to dissolve. Using electric beaters, beat egg whites until soft peaks form. Stir gelatine into yogurt mixture, then add egg whites and fold gently together until well combined, but take care not to lose the volume from the beaten egg whites. Spoon into individual serving dishes, slightly larger than 1 cup capacity each, and refrigerate for about 4 hours or until set.

ANALYSIS		4
Energy (kJ Cal)	618	147
● Carb (g)		25
● Prot (g)		10
● Fat (g)		0.5

HINT: *You may also use strawberries or blueberries in this recipe. Make sure the gelatine is well dissolved in the water before adding to the rest of the ingredients or the mousse could become lumpy and/or not set properly.*

Preparation time: 20 minutes
Cooking time: Nil

berry mousse

blueberry & apple crumble

buttermilk pancakes with maple fruit salad

"Riding off-road is never boring because every track presents new challenges. Sometimes I have to take risks and be a bit daring to get over obstacles. Meals get prepared in the same spirit. I love to try different new things or to change old recipes to make them healthier. I switch regular dairy products for low-fat varieties or halve the amount of oil in a recipe, adding other liquids to keep the dry-wet ratio the same. Through experimentation, I've learned to find the right balance to make the recipe work." MARY GRIGSON ~ mountain bike rider

blueberry & apple crumble Serves 6

800 g can pie apple
300 g frozen blueberries
1 teaspoon finely grated lemon rind (optional)
2 tablespoons caster (superfine) sugar
1 cup quick-cooking oats
$^{1}/_{2}$ cup plain (all-purpose) flour
$^{1}/_{4}$ cup brown sugar
$^{1}/_{2}$ teaspoon cinnamon
$^{1}/_{4}$ cup chopped macadamia nuts
2 tablespoons margarine, melted

Preheat oven to moderate (180°C or 350°F). Combine apple, blueberries, lemon rind and caster sugar in a 2 litre (8 cup) capacity ovenproof dish (or 6 individual 1$^{1}/_{2}$ cup capacity ovenproof dishes). Combine oats, flour, brown sugar, cinnamon and nuts in a mixing bowl. Add margarine and mix, first with a spoon then your hands, until ingredients are evenly moistened. Spread over the apple mixture. Bake for 30 minutes or until lightly browned on top.

ANALYSIS	6
Energy (kJ Cal)	1270 306
● Carb (g)	50
Prot (g)	4
● Fat (g)	10

HINT: *You can also use raw muesli (not toasted) in place of the oats. If your muesli contains nuts, you may omit the macadamia nuts from the recipe.*

Preparation time: 15 minutes
Cooking time: 30 minutes

buttermilk pancakes with maple fruit salad Serves 4-6

2 bananas, sliced
1 tablespoon lemon juice
250 g strawberries, halved
2 kiwi fruit, peeled, halved and sliced
185 mL ($^{3}/_{4}$ cup) maple syrup
4 tablespoons low-fat yogurt, to serve (optional)

PANCAKES
1$^{1}/_{2}$ cups self-raising flour
1 tablespoon caster (superfine) sugar
410 mL (1$^{2}/_{3}$ cups) buttermilk
1 egg, lightly beaten
1 teaspoon vanilla essence
light spray of canola or olive oil

Toss bananas with lemon juice as soon as they are cut. Add strawberries, kiwi fruit and maple syrup, and toss gently to combine. Set aside. To make pancakes, sift flour into a mixing bowl, stir in sugar and make a well in the centre. Whisk buttermilk, egg and vanilla together with a fork and add to the dry ingredients. Stir together until just combined (use a wire whisk or a fork) — the mixture will be slightly lumpy. Don't overbeat the mixture or the pancakes will be tough. Spray a nonstick frying pan with oil and place over medium heat. Put $^{1}/_{3}$ cup batter into the pan, and cook for about 1$^{1}/_{2}$ minutes, until bubbles appear on the surface. Turn over and cook a further 1 minute or until lightly golden underneath. Serve the pancakes topped with fruit salad, and a dollop of yogurt if desired.

ANALYSIS	4	6
Energy (kJ Cal)	2524 603	1683 402
● Carb (g)	130	87
● Prot (g)	14	10
● Fat (g)	4	2
● Calcium, Vitamin C		

HINT: *If you want everyone to eat at once, keep the cooked pancakes warm by stacking them on a plate in an oven on very low heat while you continue cooking.*

Preparation time: 20 minutes
Cooking time: 20 minutes

chocolate brownies Serves 12

$^3/_4$ cup plain (all-purpose) flour
$^3/_4$ cup self-raising flour
$^2/_3$ cup NESTLÉ Baking Cocoa
$1^1/_2$ cups caster (superfine) sugar
$^1/_3$ cup (40 g) roughly chopped walnuts
200 g carton low-fat vanilla yogurt
60 mL ($^1/_4$ cup) light olive oil
4 egg whites
2 teaspoons vanilla essence
icing sugar, to dust (optional)

Preheat oven to moderate (180°C or 350°F). Line a 30 x 20 cm shallow baking pan with aluminium foil. Sift flours and cocoa into a large bowl. Stir in sugar and walnuts, and make a well in the centre. Whisk yogurt, oil, egg whites and vanilla essence together in a small bowl. Pour onto dry ingredients, and mix lightly and quickly until just combined. Spread into prepared pan and smooth the surface. Bake for 30 minutes or until a skewer inserted into the centre of the tray comes out clean. Leave in the tin for about 15 minutes, then lift out and peel the foil away. Cut into 12 squares. Dust lightly with icing sugar before serving (optional).

ANALYSIS	12
Energy (kJ Cal)	1180 282
● Carb (g)	47
Prot (g)	6
● Fat (g)	8

HINT: *These chocolate brownies are virtually guilt free. The walnuts are optional, but add interest to the texture, and you could also use pecans instead.*

Preparation time: 15 minutes
Total cooking time: 30 minutes

chocolate brownies

"I always read food labels. I look for the sugar and fat content of the food. If a food has more than 10% fat, I am careful. Sometimes the labels are confusing and it would be good to know more. It's annoying that some of the foods that I most want to know about don't have nutrition panels."

GRANT HACKETT ~ swimmer

banana cake Serves 12

3 tablespoons margarine
$^1/_2$ cup caster (superfine) sugar
3 large ripe bananas, chopped
2 eggs
1 teaspoon vanilla essence
1 cup self-raising flour
1 cup wholemeal self-raising flour
185 mL ($^3/_4$ cup) buttermilk

ICING (optional)
$^3/_4$ cup icing sugar
1 tablespoon lemon juice
2-4 teaspoons boiling water

Preheat oven to moderate (180°C or 350°F). Lightly grease a 20 cm round cake pan, and line the base with baking paper. Using electric beaters, beat margarine, sugar and bananas until well combined and banana is almost smooth. Add the eggs one at a time, beating well after each addition, then beat in the vanilla. Sift flours into the bowl, and pour in milk. Fold in quickly and lightly until just combined, but do not overbeat or the cake will be tough. Pour into prepared pan, and bake for about 70 minutes or until a skewer or knife inserted into the centre of the cake comes out clean. Leave in the pan for 5 minutes before turning out onto a wire rack to cool. If you are icing the cake, wait until it is completely cooled. Sift icing sugar into a bowl and stir in juice and enough water to make a thin icing. Spread over the cake and leave to set.

ANALYSIS	12
Energy (kJ Cal)	967 231
● Carb (g)	41
Prot (g)	5
● Fat (g)	5

HINT: *Buttermilk is used for low-fat baking. It is cultured (like yogurt), and therefore quite acidic which makes the cake tender and moist.*

Preparation time: 20 minutes
Cooking time: 1 hour 10 minutes

banana cake

apricot & date slice

apple strudel

"Most nights I enjoy eating something sweet after dinner. I don't often have a lot of time on my hands, so I normally have some tinned fruit with rice custard, low-fat custard or yogurt. One of my favourites is dipping plain sweet biscuits into vanilla low-fat yoghurt. When I have the time, I really enjoy baking a cake — my speciality is Apple Lumberjack cake. You'll have to wait for the next edition of this book for that recipe." PETER SOROS ~ waterpolo player

apricot & date slice Serves 12

FILLING

1¹/₃ cups (250 g) pitted dates, chopped
1¹/₃ cups (250 g) dried apricots, chopped
250 mL (1 cup) water
¹/₂ cup (30 g) shredded coconut

PASTRY

2 cups rolled oats
1 cup wholemeal plain (all-purpose) flour
¹/₂ cup raw sugar
4 tablespoons margarine, melted
80 mL (¹/₃ cup) water

Preheat the oven to moderately hot (200°C or 400°F). Line a 30 x 20 cm shallow baking pan with foil. To make filling, put dates and apricots in a small saucepan and add the water. Bring to the boil, reduce heat to low and cook for 3–4 minutes, stirring frequently, until fruit is pulpy and water has been absorbed. Stir in coconut and set aside to cool. To make pastry, combine oats, flour and sugar in a mixing bowl, and make a well in the centre. Add margarine and water, and mix with a knife until ingredients are evenly moistened. Press half the pastry into the prepared pan, spreading firmly with the back of a spoon. Spread filling over pastry, sprinkle remaining pastry evenly over the top and press lightly with a fork. Bake for 30 minutes or until golden brown. Cool in the pan then lift out and cut into squares to serve. Garnish with toasted shredded coconut or a light dusting of icing sugar if desired.

ANALYSIS	12
Energy (kJ Cal)	1268 362
● Carb (g)	53
Prot (g)	5
● Fat (g)	8

HINT: *This slice makes a nice sweet to have with tea or coffee, and is great for packing in a lunch box or picnic basket.*

Preparation time: 20 minutes
Cooking time: 40 minutes

apple strudel Serves 4-6

800 g can pie apple
2 tablespoons raw sugar
¹/₂ teaspoon cinnamon
¹/₂ cup sultanas
¹/₄ cup chopped walnuts (optional)
4 sheets filo pastry
1 tablespoon skim milk, approximately
1 tablespoon icing sugar

Preheat oven to hot (210°C or 415°F). Lightly grease a flat baking tray. Put apple in a bowl and mix with sugar, cinnamon, sultanas and walnuts. Brush a sheet of filo pastry very lightly with milk, and top with another sheet. Brush this sheet, and top with another sheet. Brush this sheet and top with the last sheet, but do not brush this one. Lay the pastry out with the long edges at front and back, short edges at the sides. Place apple mix in a neat log shape across the pastry, leaving clear about 12 cm on either side and 10 cm at the front and back. Fold the sides over the filling then fold the front and back to enclose. Carefully place on prepared tray, seam-side down, and make 4 fine cuts diagonally across the top. Bake for 20 minutes or until golden brown. Dust with icing sugar and serve immediately.

ANALYSIS	4	6
Energy (kJ Cal)	1200 287	800 191
● Carb (g)	56	37
Prot (g)	4	3
● Fat (g)	6	4

HINT: *Eat this straight away as the pastry becomes soft on standing. When using filo, work quickly and keep the pastry covered until it is needed as it becomes dry and brittle very fast.*

Preparation time: 15 minutes
Cooking time: 20 minutes

fruity bread pudding   Serves 4-6

10 slices of raisin bread
$^1/_4$ cup raspberry jam
3 egg whites
250 mL (1 cup) CARNATION Light and Creamy Evaporated Milk
600 mL ($2^1/_2$ cups) low-fat custard
$^1/_4$ teaspoon nutmeg

Preheat oven to moderate (180°C or 350°F). Spread the bread with jam, and cut each slice diagonally into quarters. Arrange in layers in a 2 litre (8 cup) capacity ovenproof dish. Whisk egg whites, milk and custard together and pour over the bread, coating each piece. Sprinkle with nutmeg, and bake for 30–40 minutes or until golden brown and the custard has set. Cover surface with foil if pudding is becoming too browned. Serve with extra low-fat custard if desired.

ANALYSIS	4	6
Energy (kJ Cal)	1662 397	1107 265
● Carb (g)	71	47
● Prot (g)	17	11
● Fat (g)	6	4
● Calcium		

HINT: *You can replace raisin bread with ordinary sliced bread, and ½ cup sultanas and ¼ teaspoon ground cinnamon sprinkled among the layers. Use any flavour of jam you like.*

Preparation time: 10 minutes
Cooking time: 30-40 minutes

fruity bread pudding

> " Cooking is one of my favourite pastimes. I say that it's my therapy. If there is a lot of mess, it is usually an indication that it will taste great. The only problem is my pet hate is washing up."

SIMONE HANKIN ~ water polo player

chocolate self-saucing pudding   Serves 6

$1^1/_2$ cups self-raising flour
1 tablespoon NESTLÉ Baking Cocoa
$^2/_3$ cup caster (superfine) sugar
1 egg
2 tablespoons margarine, melted
250 mL (1 cup) skim milk

SAUCE
2 tablespoons NESTLÉ Baking Cocoa
$^1/_2$ cup caster (superfine) sugar
315 mL ($1^1/_4$ cups) boiling water

Preheat oven to moderate (180°C or 350°F). Sift flour and cocoa into a large bowl, stir in sugar and make a well in the centre. Whisk egg, margarine and milk together, and pour onto dry ingredients. Stir gently until just combined, but don't beat vigorously or the pudding will be tough. Spread pudding mix into a 2 litre (8 cup) capacity ovenproof dish. To make the sauce, dissolve cocoa and sugar in the boiling water. Gently pour onto pudding mix. Bake for 40 minutes or until a knife comes out clean when inserted into the pudding (not through to the sauce at the bottom). To microwave this pudding, use a round microwave-safe dish and cook on HIGH for 10 minutes. Test and if not ready cook for a further 2 minutes. Serve with low-fat custard or low-fat ice cream.

ANALYSIS	6
Energy (kJ Cal)	1517 362
● Carb (g)	77
Prot (g)	7
● Fat (g)	4

HINT: *This decadent dessert will impress any chocolate lover. Just remember to serve with a low-fat cream or ice cream. It's a great dessert for winter dinner parties.*

Preparation time: 15 minutes
Cooking time: 40 minutes

chocolate self-saucing pudding

Drinks can be real energy boosters as well as sweet treats. Experiment with different fruits in season, or keep canned fruits such as peaches or mango on hand for convenience. Also, try different flavours of low-fat yogurt. For those who are lactose intolerant or just dislike dairy products, the milk and yogurt can be replaced with soy milk and soy yogurt but just remember to choose the low-fat varieties. The following recipes each make about 1–2 large drinks and all use the same method of preparation — just put all the ingredients in the blender, blend until frothy, then drink immediately.

heavenly chocolate malted Serves 1

250 mL (1 cup) skim milk
1 scoop NESTLÉ PETERS Light and Creamy Chocolate
   Swirl Ice Cream
1 tablespoon NESQUIK Chocolate Powder
2 tablespoons NESTLÉ Malted Milk Powder

ANALYSIS	1 glass
Energy (kJ Cal)	964 230
● Carb (g)	34
● Prot (g)	14
● Fat (g)	5
● Calcium	

peach mango thickshake Serves 2

250 mL (1 cup) skim milk
1 scoop NESTLÉ PETERS Light and Creamy Ice Cream
200 g carton low-fat peach mango yogurt
½ cup sliced peaches in natural juice, drained

ANALYSIS	1 glass
Energy (kJ Cal)	697 160
● Carb (g)	28
● Prot (g)	10
● Fat (g)	2
● Calcium	

any fruit smoothie Serves 2

250 mL (1 cup) skim milk
200 g carton low-fat vanilla yogurt
2 tablespoons skim milk powder (optional)
2 tablespoons wheat germ (optional)
Any one of the following fruit portions:
   1 large ripe banana
   ½ cup strawberries
   1 peeled large peach
   1 peeled small mango

ANALYSIS	1 glass
Energy (kJ Cal)	908 217
● Carb (g)	36
● Prot (g)	16
● Fat (g)	1
● Calcium	

tropical fruit freezy Serves 2

250 mL (1 cup) tropical fruit juice
200 g carton low-fat mango yogurt
1 large ripe banana
4 ice cubes (optional)

ANALYSIS	I glass
Energy (kJ Cal)	773 184
● Carb (g)	38
● Prot (g)	6
● Fat (g)	1
● Calcium	

peach mango thickshake

heavenly chocolate malted

any fruit smoothie

tropical fruit freezy

eating on the run ~ planning meals over the day

It is one thing to cook your own meals, but a winning diet means planning the whole day's eating and taking into account training and competition needs and the lifestyle commitments that go with your sport. This requires both organisation and creativity.

ideas for breakfast

Breakfast is a great incentive to get out of bed in the morning or it's a delicious refuelling stop after your first training session of the day. Either way, high-carbohydrate, low-fat eating is easily found in breakfast menus that range from quick and portable to relaxed and exotic.

- Breakfast cereals — especially wholegrain types
- Porridge or oatmeal
- Bircher muesli (see recipe)
- Reduced-fat fruit yogurt
- Fruit dairy snack or fromage fraise
- Fresh fruit or canned fruit
- Toast, muffins or crumpets with jam, honey or Vegemite
- Fruit juice
- Skim milk hot chocolate

For a Hot Breakfast
- Porridge or oatmeal
- Pancakes or waffles
- Baked beans on toast
- Spaghetti on toast
- Omelette or scrambled eggs on toast
- Creamed corn on toast

Something Quick or to Eat on the Move
- A fuel-packed smoothie
- Fruit
- Carton of yogurt or fruit dairy snack
- Breakfast or cereal bar
- Fruit muffin (but watch the fat content)

> **BIRCHER MUESLI**
>
> 2 cups oats
> 200 g carton reduced fat berry-flavoured yogurt
> 150 mL (½ cup) low-fat milk
> ½ cup sultanas
> 150 mL (½ cup) orange juice
> punnet of strawberries (½ can boysenberries, optional)
>
> Soak oats overnight with berry-flavoured yogurt, low-fat milk, sultanas and orange juice. Before serving, cut strawberries or other berries and stir through. Sprinkle with slivered almonds.

ideas for lunch

Most busy athletes have to eat lunch on the run. Those with more time can enjoy a hot meal, but it is a far cry from the infamous business lunch. Lunch is a chance to top up for the afternoon training session and, in some cases, to prepare for an evening match or competition. Some athletes who compete at night turn their day around to have their main meal at lunch and a lighter snack post-game.

- Sandwiches made with bread, bagels, focaccia, rolls or pita bread — explore the huge varieties of bread available
- Toasted sandwiches or jaffles
- Homemade pizzas
- Main meal soup and bread
- Main meal salad and bread
- Baked potato with filling
- Leftovers (reheated if necessary)
- Fresh fruit
- Fruit salad and frozen yogurt
- Fruit-style muffins (but watch the fat content)
- Cereal bar
- Pikelets, scones or fruit buns
- Reduced-fat fruit yogurt or fruit dairy snack
- Fruit juice
- Skim milk hot chocolate
- Fruit smoothie

> **IDEAS FOR SANDWICH FILLINGS**
> - Spread of avocado, barbecue or roast chicken breast meat, alfalfa sprouts and tomato
> - Roast turkey, cranberry sauce, tomato, green capsicum and lettuce
> - Light spread of peanut butter, grated carrot, sultanas, grated reduced-fat cheese
> - Spread of chutney, lean ham, sliced pineapple, red capsicum and alfalfa sprouts
> - Light spread of peanut butter, sliced apple and sultanas
> - Vegemite, grated reduced-fat cheese, finely chopped celery and gourmet lettuce
> - Spread of salsa, sliced avocado, red capsicum, baked beans (this is a great toasted sandwich or jaffle)
> - Light mayonnaise mixed with tinned prawns, finely chopped celery and lettuce
> - Spread of avocado, tinned or fresh salmon slices, green capsicum

ideas for dinner

Traditionally, most of us eat our heartiest meal at night, and while some diet books have suggested this is wrong and have promoted lighter evening meals, this is often unsuitable for athletes. For many athletes, dinner is the first meal after the main training session of the day so refuelling and rehydrating are important goals to cater for and the menu needs to be high in carbohydrate. Hungry athletes may want a hearty and substantial meal, while others may prefer a lighter meal that won't weigh them down when they fall into bed shortly after eating. The versatility of foods rich in carbohydrate means that all needs and appetites can be catered for.

This book has focused on various styles of cooking that make carbohydrate foods the centre of attention, adding a small amount of lean protein and plenty of vegetables to balance the meal. Sometimes, it is a matter of cooking separate items, but you should dish out the carbohydrate foods first so that they take up most room on the plate. Most of the recipes for 'all in one pot' meals contain the right balance of ingredients within the single meal, and they are an almost foolproof way to eat.

Main Meal Ideas
- Curries or spicy meals with rice or couscous
- Risotto, paella, pilaf and rice dishes
- Pasta with sauce
- Baked pasta dishes (e.g. lasagne) with added bread or salad to balance
- Stirfry with pasta, noodles, rice or couscous
- Main meal soup with bread
- Main meal salad with bread
- Baked potato with filling
- Homemade pizza with creative toppings
- Grilled meat (such as steak, chicken breasts, kebabs) balanced with salad and vegetables and a large serve of bread, potato, rice or pasta
- Dry roasted meats balanced with baked potatoes, bread and steamed vegetables

Dessert Ideas
- Rice pudding
- Bread and butter pudding
- Fruit crumbles
- Fruit strudels made with filo pastry
- Pancakes or waffles
- Stewed fruit
- Canned fruit in natural juice
- Reduced-fat ice cream
- Low-fat frozen yogurt
- Sorbet and gelati
- Reduced-fat fruit yogurts
- Fruit dairy snack or fromage frais
- Low-fat custards
- Cake or muffins (but watch the fat content)
- Low-fat mousses and fruit whips
- Pikelets, scones or fruit buns
- Skim milk hot chocolate

ideas for snacks

Eating between meals has gathered a bad reputation. Snacks are claimed to ruin your appetite, make you fat and cause tooth decay. Frequent eating does take a toll on your teeth so keep your brush or some sugar-free gum handy, but the other charges against snacks don't hold up when good choices are made. In fact, healthy snacks are an essential part of a winning diet for athletes.

Athletes with high-energy needs must eat more than three times each day to achieve their kilojoule and carbohydrate requirements. The most successful way to achieve a high energy intake is to increase the number of times you eat rather than the size of the meal.

Snacks are also suitable for athletes with low-energy needs. A light snack before training can top up fuel levels and help you train well. This is much better than feeling faint and hungry throughout your work out, then returning home ravenous and eating the pantry bare.

Convenient carbohydrate options enhance post-exercise recovery for athletes with heavy training and competition schedules. When it is impractical to have your next meal within the first hour post-exercise, a well-chosen snack can start the refuelling process until you next full meal (the "carbohydrate cavalry") can be consumed.

On a busy day, it may be impossible to stop for a traditional meal break. A series of snacks can provide the same value, and be easier to eat on the run.

GOOD SNACKS

SUBSTANTIAL
- Toasted sandwiches or jaffles with fruit juice
- Leftovers warmed up and served with bread or on toast
- Fruit salad and frozen yogurt topping
- Baked beans or canned spaghetti on toast
- Large bowl of cereal with reduced-fat milk and fresh or canned fruit
- Large fruit smoothie with toast, bagel or English muffins and toppings
- Sandwiches with chunky fillings

A LIGHT TOP-UP
- Small bowl of cereal with reduced-fat milk or yogurt
- Carton of reduced fat fruit yogurt or fruit dairy snack and a piece of fruit
- Skim milk hot chocolate or milk coffee with toast or English muffin
- Cereal bar and piece of fruit
- Rice cakes with sliced banana or light cream cheese or cottage cheese toppings
- Pikelets, scones or fruit bun
- Fruit smoothie

EAT ON THE RUN
- Liquid meal supplement
- Breakfast bars
- Sandwiches
- Fresh fruit
- Dried fruit and nut mixes
- Fruit muffin, fruit bun, scone or pikelet
- Reduced-fat fruit yogurt or fromage frais

tips for travelling

Travelling can broaden experiences and fill up a passport, but it also presents a new array of eating challenges to athletes. These include disruptions to usual training and eating schedules, changes to food availability, changes in climate, and the excitement and distractions of a new environment. The following ideas will help you to take your winning diet with you, wherever you go.

Plan Ahead

- Contact the airline to find out what meal services will be provided. Sometimes you may want to arrange special meals suited to your requirements (this must be done well in advance). Check what is in the 'athlete meals', 'low-fat meals' or 'vegetarian meals' on offer as sometimes these are not what they seem.
- Investigate the availability of food at your destination as thoroughly as possible before leaving home. Try to find out the location of shops and restaurants and their opening hours, as well as the self-catering or food storage facilities at your accommodation.
- Find out your daily schedule so that you can plan meals around this. Often, training or competitions will clash with your normal meal and snack times, and a new or flexible food schedule will be needed.
- With this information, make a general plan of where, when and what you will eat. Try to stick to your usual meal pattern as much as possible while away, but be prepared for changes.
- Take your own food or snacks to replace the key items you may not be able to find at your destination (see list).
- Carry a selection of snack foods with you at all times. Do not let yourself get too hungry or you are likely to be tempted by the first fast-food outlet you see.

USEFUL FOOD FOR TRAVELLING
- breakfast bars
- breakfast cereal + powdered milk
- snack-pack fruits
- dried fruit
- two-minute noodles (look for low-fat versions)
- rice cakes
- jam, honey, peanut butter, Vegemite
- powdered sports drink
- powdered liquid meal supplements
- baked beans
- canned spaghetti

Eat and Drink Well When on the Move

The unglamourous part of travel is having to sit still for long periods. Forced inactivity, increased fluid loss, low-fibre diets and changes in time zone can lead to increased dehydration and sluggish digestion. This may interfere with your performance for the first few days after arrival, but on tours where you are constantly on the road, it can become a significant chronic problem. Boredom eating while inactive can also add up to unwanted weight gain.

- Planes are particularly dehydrating, but fluid loss can also increase in airconditioned buses or hot environments. You will need to drink regularly to counteract this loss. Carry a water bottle with you on trips and drink to your own schedule rather than when beverage services are provided.
- Avoid alcohol on planes, and be wary of relying only on caffeine-containing fluids (tea, coffee, cola drinks) to keep hydrated. Water, mineral water, juices, soft drinks or sports drinks are the best fluid choices.
- Don't confuse boredom with hunger. Plan your food intake in advance and decide which meals you need, and whether your own snacks are also required. Stick to this plan. Don't be tempted by all the meal services offered on plane flights, or the shops visited during stops on bus trips.
- On long-haul flights, adopt the meal pattern that you will have at your destination — for example, accept only the meals that coincide with breakfast and dinner

times at your new location. This might see you sleeping through some of the plane meals, but as well as benefitting from extra sleep, you will speed up the adjustment of your body clock.

- Carry some higher fibre snacks (wholemeal breakfast bars or dried fruit) if you suffer from constipation on long journeys and keep well hydrated.

Be Wary of Food and Water Hygiene

Many countries have lower standards of hygiene and water purity than we enjoy, and the resulting gastric reactions can cause a major impairment of performance as well as spoil the fun of overseas travel.

- Find out whether it is safe to drink the local water supply. If it isn't, keep to bottled water or drinks served in sealed containers. Be wary of ice added to drinks in case it is made from tap water, and even clean your teeth using your bottled water supplies. Some athletes stick to these rules in all new environments, at least for the first few days.
- In high-risk environments, keep to food served in the restaurants of good hotels, or well-known food franchises. Avoid eating food from street stalls and local markets, however inviting and authentic it seems. You should also avoid fruit, unless it can be peeled, and fresh salads. Only eat foods that are well cooked and be wary of local seafood and ice cream.

Use Takeaway Food Well

Takeaway food can be a cheap and convenient option while travelling. Often, takeaway outlets are the only shops open, or the cleanest and safest food supplier. Although many takeaway food choices are high in fat and low on fuel, there are still good choices to be made. In general, look for chains or outlets that let you make your own order instead of those which serve standard products. Salad bars are ideal, but avoid 'meal deals' which, although cheap, see you eating extra fries or fatty desserts that you don't really need. Good choices are:

- bread rolls or sandwiches with plenty of salad, lean meat fillings and no margarine.
- pizza — choose thick crust varieties and vegetarian or lean-meat toppings, and ask for less cheese.
- hamburgers — make sure they are grilled and have plenty of salad added. Choose tomato sauce rather than mayonnaise or creamy dressings, and avoid extras such as double meat, fried eggs, bacon or cheese.
- Asian food — make steamed rice the meal base and add stirfries with vegetables and lean meats. Avoid battered and deep-fried dishes, including most appetisers.
- Mexican — fajitas (corn tortillas around grilled beef, chicken or seafood), and rice, salad and salsa. Avoid excessive cheese and sour cream.
- souvlaki
- baked potato — avoid butter, sour cream
- hearty vegetable-filled soups with bread
- low-fat smoothies
- low-fat frozen yogurt with fruit toppings or fruit salad
- fresh fruit
- plain mineral water or juices
- skim milk hot chocolate or cappuccino

Restaurant Eating

Although restaurants can be expensive when you are on a budget, you may find yourself in a situation where you can cater for your own breakfasts and lunches and eat out in the evenings. Most restaurants provide a varied menu that caters for high-carbohydrate low-fat eating, although you may need to make some special requests.

- Make sure that your water glass is topped up regularly to help with hydration goals. For extra carbohydrate, soft drinks or fruit juice may also be good.
- Choose meals that focus on carbohydrate choices such as rice or pasta. In the case of pasta dishes, go for tomato-based sauces rather than cream-based sauces. Risotto or paella are good choices as long as there is not too much oil in the cooking.
- Asian food offers lots of possibilities. Fill your plate or bowl with steamed rice or plain noodles and choose a main dish based on lean meat, fish or chicken and plenty of vegetables. Avoid dishes that are deep-fried or battered.
- If you are having a main course based on meat, fish or poultry, choose a medium-sized portion and don't forget the fuel foods such as a baked potato or a side dish of rice. Get the bread basket topped up.
- Order side serves of vegetables or salad if they don't come with the meal. Ask for black pepper, tomato sauce or salsa rather than buttery sauces, and lemon juice rather than salad dressings.
- Carbohydrate-rich desserts include rice pudding, bread and butter pudding, sorbet, fruit salad or fruit crumble. If you're watching your total energy intake, finish up with a fruit platter or skim milk hot chocolate.

Planning Ahead to Look After a Team

Feeding a team can be a logistical nightmare, especially when events finish late at night. It can be hard for restaurants to handle large numbers and individual meal requests quickly.

- Book a restaurant ahead of time and negotiate a menu. It also helps to ring ahead to fine-tune your arrival time so that food will be ready as you walk in the door.
- Buffet eating is recommended — it's quick for hungry athletes, cost-saving when negotiating prices with the restaurant, and offers flexibility so that each athlete can choose the type and amount of food that they need.
- Plan a menu based on carbohydrate-rich dishes and offer sufficient choice to meet the preferences of the majority of your athletes. Note that too much choice encourages overeating, because people try a little bit of everything. If you are away for more than a week, put effort into increasing the variety from day to day, rather than within the same meal.
- Make separate arrangements for athletes with special needs (i.e. vegetarians or those with food intolerances). It is hard to accommodate all needs within one menu, so be prepared to arrange special needs as required.
- Remember that snacks are part of the dietary plan and are often neglected when catering arrangements provide for three meals a day. Provide items at meals that can be taken away for eating later — for example fruit, cartons of yogurt, muffins and breakfast bars. Alternatively, organise a communal room with a fridge so you have somewhere to put these snack items, and other choices such as breakfast cereal.

self-catering

Many small groups or individuals choose to stay in apartments and do their own cooking when away on trips. This can be an economical choice that offers flexibility with meal times and food selections.

However, just as with cooking at home, it can be hard to have the motivation and appetite to prepare a meal when you are exhausted from your event or training, and there are added problems with organising menus for limited stays. It is also hard to coordinate dishes that can be made from a limited number of ingredients, and often you end up with leftovers or leftover ingredients or find that your favourite dish doesn't taste the same without that pinch of something you don't have.

Quick and easy meals that require a minimum number of ingredients and equipment are essential, and the following menus solve these difficulties. Firstly, we have provided a full menu plan for a week, in which meal selections are balanced and co-ordinated to use up all the leftovers. The second menu plan caters for evening meals only, and mixes and matches the recipes so that all ingredients are used. For both the plans we've included a shopping list of all the things you need.

Notes on the Shopping Lists
- If you want to really save time, contact the local supermarket at your destination and ask if they will collect and deliver your shopping needs. Fax the shopping list in advance of your trip, and arrange for the basic ingredients to be delivered shortly before or after your arrival.
- Note that some ingredients need to be purchased fresh or later in the week rather than at the time of your arrival. These ingredients are marked with an asterix* in the shopping list.
- Snacks are variable according to the individuals, and while we have included some snack ideas, you should add them to the list according to your requirements.
- Take advantage of the local or seasonal produce such as fresh fruit and vegetables or bread at your destination and adjust the shopping list accordingly.
- Under 'miscellaneous' in the shopping list are many foods (like honey and hot drinks) that you should choose according to individual preferences. The sauces, seasonings or herbs (with the required amount in brackets) may be purchased new with the other supplies, or you might want to take your own. These can be placed into little jars, plastic bags or tubes (such as clean film cannisters) and then the whole lot packed into a larger airtight container. You can also leave some of the sauces, herbs and seasonings out of the recipes, or substitute according to what's available.

seven-day menu plan

This menu plan will provide four athletes with three meals per day (breakfast, lunch and dinner) for a week. The recipes are marked with the page numbers for easy reference.

All you have to do is:
- Check the menu plan (making any changes you need to adjust for special preferences and for the individual items such as snacks).
- If possible, check the availability of cooking equipment in your apartment. You may need to adjust the recipes if important equipment is missing. Alternatively, you can take a time-saving or versatile piece of cooking equipment with you.
- Pack your *Survival for the Fittest* cookbook.
- Follow the shopping list and buy the ingredients.

Equipment
- stove top
- oven
- nonstick frying pan or wok (or electric frying pan or wok)
- large saucepans
- deep lasagne dish
- cake tin
- microwave
- microwave dishes
- wooden spoon or large plastic spoons
- wooden skewers

shopping list

Bread
- [ ] 7 loaves bread (vary according to your preferences)★
- [ ] packet of pita bread or 4 foccacia rolls★
- [ ] 4 crusty bread rolls★
- [ ] 20 bread rolls★
- [ ] 4 packets pikelets★
- [ ] 8 tortillas★

Fruit and Vegetables
- [ ] 16 bananas
- [ ] 20 apples
- [ ] 20 oranges
- [ ] 12 tomatoes
- [ ] 3 lettuces
- [ ] 1 head of broccoli
- [ ] 6 onions + 2 red onions
- [ ] 1 carrot
- [ ] 3 red capsicum
- [ ] 1 yellow capsicum
- [ ] 1 green capsicum
- [ ] 1 small sweet potato (kumera)
- [ ] 14 large washed potatoes
- [ ] 2 zucchini (courgette)
- [ ] salad ingredients (lettuce, tomatoes, carrot, cucumber)
- [ ] 120 g mushrooms
- [ ] 1 punnet cherry tomatoes
- [ ] 2 punnets raspberries (tinned if not in season)
- [ ] 2 punnets strawberries
- [ ] 1 lemon (optional)

Dairy and Refrigerated Products
- [ ] 5 litres reduced-fat milk★
- [ ] 2 x 200 g carton low-fat natural yogurt
- [ ] 7 x 1 litre cartons fruit-flavoured low-fat yogurt
- [ ] 2 x 1 litre low-fat custard
- [ ] 500 g grated reduced-fat cheese
- [ ] tub of canola margarine
- [ ] 2 packets fresh lasagne sheets
- [ ] 2 large pizza bases (covered in tomato paste)
- [ ] 8 litres orange juice

Meat and Eggs
- [ ] 400 g sliced lean ham
- [ ] 1.6 kg lean mince
- [ ] 300 g lean lamb mince
- [ ] 1 kg lean beef cut into strips
- [ ] 8 chicken breasts
- [ ] 2 large barbecue chickens
- [ ] 12 eggs

Canned and Packet Goods
- [ ] 3 x 500 g packets breakfast cereal
- [ ] 500 g packet rice
- [ ] 500 g pasta shells
- [ ] 2 x 440 g cans kidney beans
- [ ] 5 x 420 g cans fruit in natural juices
- [ ] 3 x 450 g cans spaghetti
- [ ] 2 x 450 g cans tuna in water or brine
- [ ] 2 x 560 g or large can tomato soup
- [ ] 330 g can chickpeas
- [ ] 300 g corn kernals
- [ ] 3 x 375 mL cans CARNATION Light and Creamy Evaporated Milk
- [ ] 3 x 425 g cans crushed tomatoes
- [ ] 3 x bottles or jars of pasta sauce
- [ ] 2 x 440 g cans boysenberries
- [ ] 440 g can pineapple
- [ ] 800 g can pie apple
- [ ] 100 g dry-roasted cashews
- [ ] 200 g slivered almonds
- [ ] packet pancake mix
- [ ] 500 g self-raising flour
- [ ] 500 g plain (all-purpose) flour
- [ ] 500 g packet sugar
- [ ] NESTLÉ Baking Cocoa (3 tablespoons)
- [ ] jar of minced garlic
- [ ] jar of green curry paste (1 tablespoon)
- [ ] small bottle soy sauce
- [ ] spray-on canola oil
- [ ] small tub of tomato paste
- [ ] bottle of coconut essence
- [ ] packet of cornflour
- [ ] 50 g of macadamia nuts
- [ ] small packet of cooking oats

Frozen Items
- [ ] 500 g packet Asian stirfry vegetable mix
- [ ] 500 g packet mixed vegetables
- [ ] 2 litres NESTLÉ PETERS Light and Creamy Ice Cream or 2 x 1 litre frozen sorbet or fruit dessert★

Miscellaneous (optional)
- [ ] minced ginger (1 teaspoon)
- [ ] low-oil salad dressings
- [ ] salt
- [ ] black pepper
- [ ] cinnamon (1/2 teaspoon)
- [ ] mustard for sandwiches
- [ ] mixed herbs (2 teaspoons)
- [ ] MAGGI Sweet Chilli Sauce (4 tablespoons)
- [ ] cumin (2 teaspoons)
- [ ] coriander (2 teaspoons)
- [ ] tandoori mix (1 tablespoon)
- [ ] Vegemite
- [ ] 500 g honey
- [ ] 500 g jam
- [ ] 500 g maple syrup
- [ ] tea
- [ ] NESCAFÉ coffee
- [ ] Drinking chocolate or MILO
- [ ] lemon juice (2 tablespoons)

Snack Ideas (quantities will vary for individuals)
- [ ] cereal bars
- [ ] loaf bread★
- [ ] English-style muffins or crumpets
- [ ] seasonal fruit★
- [ ] 200 g cartons low-fat fruit yogurt
- [ ] reduced-fat milk
- [ ] 500 g packets breakfast cereal

MEAL	DAY 1	DAY 2	DAY 3	DAY 4	DAY 5	DAY 6	DAY 7
Breakfast	Cereal, low-fat milk or fruit yogurt, toast and fruit, orange juice	Eggs and tomato on toast / orange juice	Cereal, low-fat milk or fruit yogurt, toast and fruit, orange juice	Tinned spaghetti on toast / orange juice	Cereal, low-fat milk or yogurt, toast and fruit, orange juice	Cereal, low-fat milk or yogurt, toast and fruit / orange juice	Pancakes (from mix), maple syrup and fruit / orange juice
Lunch	Sandwiches or bread rolls with salad and ham, barbecue chicken or tuna / fresh fruit	Toasted sandwiches (cheese and tomato) or fresh soup in winter (optional) / fresh fruit	Lasagne (leftovers from day 1) / fresh fruit	Sandwiches or bread rolls with salad and ham, chicken or tuna / fresh fruit	Jacket potatoes with spicy bean sauce and salad / fresh fruit	Sandwiches or bread rolls with salad and ham, chicken or tuna / fresh fruit	Chicken breast hamburgers served with salad
Dinner	Louise's secret lasagne (make double the amount and top with a large can of tomato soup) (page 61)	Quick vegetarian curry (page 73)	Quick pasta casserole (page 61)	Spicy bean burritos (make a double batch of recipe) (page 29)	Beef with cashew stirfry (page 70)	Barbecue night: tandoori chicken (minus skewers), beef and capsicum kebabs (page 84)	Pizza night: ham and pineapple (use up left over vegetables) (page 94)
Accompaniments	Vegetables	Rice	Bread rolls	Salad	Rice	Pita bread, jacket potatoes and salad	Salad and bread
Dessert	Chocolate self-saucing pudding, custard (page 110)	Pikelets and canned fruit, ice cream	Make an exotic fruit salad with canned and fresh berries and sprinkled with almonds	Ice cream and canned fruit	Pikelets and canned fruit, ice cream	Exotic fruit salad, ice cream	Blueberry and apple crumble, and custard (page 105)
Snacks	Fruit, cereal bars, English-style muffins or crumpets, yogurt, cereal, bread (as required)						

quick and easy dinner menu

On some camps or tours, you are left to cater for your own evening meals, while breakfast and lunches are quickly provided through cereals, toast and fruit, and sandwiches, yogurt and fruit.

The following menu, for four people, has been modified for very quick and easy cooking – minimal preparation (20 minutes), cost and number of individual ingredients. Desserts are taken care of by prepared items that can be purchased from the supermarket. The recipes have been adapted so they use up all the ingredients you've bought and you won't have to worry about leftovers or wasted food, and a recipe card has also been included.

All you have to do is:
- Check that the recipe suggestions suit your needs and make alterations as necessary.
- If possible, check what cooking equipment is available at your accommodation.
- Do the shopping from the list.
- Pack *Survival for the Fittest* or photocopy the recipe card for the adapted recipes to take with you.

DAY	DINNER	DESSERT
1	Beef and vegetable stirfry	Low-fat fruit yogurts
2	No-fuss spaghetti bolognese	Exotic fruit salad (with berries and almonds)
3	Chicken and corn risotto	Rice pudding (pre-prepared) and tinned fruit
4	Spicy meat burritos	Fruit dairy snacks
5	Chicken burgers	Pikelets with maple syrup and reduced-fat ice cream
6	Pasta with creamy ham sauce	Bananas with custard
7	Pizza night	Jelly (pre-prepared) and reduced-fat ice cream

shopping list

Bread
- [ ] 8 large tortillas
- [ ] 8 crusty rolls
- [ ] 2 packets pikelets

Fruit and Vegetables
- [ ] 5 onions
- [ ] 2 red capsicums
- [ ] 1 green capsicum
- [ ] 1 lettuce
- [ ] 6 tomatoes
- [ ] 250 g button mushrooms
- [ ] 4 bananas
- [ ] salad ingredients (lettuce, tomato, cucumber, avocado)
- [ ] 1 carrot
- [ ] head of broccoli

Dairy and Refrigerated Products
- [ ] 500 g grated reduced-fat cheese
- [ ] 2 large pizza bases (with tomato-based sauce)
- [ ] 1 x 200 g tub natural low-fat yogurt
- [ ] 1 litre low-fat fruit yogurt
- [ ] 1 litre rice pudding
- [ ] 4 x fruit dairy snacks
- [ ] 1 litre low-fat custard

Meat
- [ ] 1 kg lean mince
- [ ] 400 g chicken breast fillets (cut into strips)
- [ ] 4 chicken breast (halves)
- [ ] 200 g lean ham
- [ ] 500 g premium lean beef (cut for stirfry)
- [ ] 1 barbecue chicken

Canned and Packet Goods
- [ ] spray canola or olive oil
- [ ] 2 x 500 g packets pasta
- [ ] 2 x 575 g jars pasta sauce
- [ ] 250 g dried thin egg noodles
- [ ] packet arborio rice (1½ cups)
- [ ] packet cornflour (1 tablespoon)
- [ ] 400 g can boysenberries
- [ ] 400 g can raspberries
- [ ] 440 g can red kidney beans
- [ ] 425 g can baby corn
- [ ] 825 g can fruit in natural juices
- [ ] 525 mL can CARNATION Light and Creamy Evaporated Milk
- [ ] packet jelly crystals
- [ ] 400 g can pineapple pieces
- [ ] small can beetroot
- [ ] 1 litre MAGGI Chicken Stock

Frozen Items
- [ ] 1 litre NESTLÉ PETERS Light and Creamy Ice Cream or 1 litre frozen sorbet or fruit dessert
- [ ] 500 g packet Asian stirfry vegetables
- [ ] 500 g packet mixed vegetables

Miscellaneous
- [ ] jar minced garlic (2 teaspoons)
- [ ] jar minced ginger (2 teaspoons)
- [ ] plum sauce (¼ cup)
- [ ] MAGGI Sweet Chilli Sauce (2 tablespoons)
- [ ] fresh parsley (2 tablespoons), optional
- [ ] fresh basil (2 tablespoons), optional
- [ ] 100 g slivered almonds
- [ ] maple syrup
- [ ] oil-free salad dressing
- [ ] black pepper
- [ ] salt

DAY 1
beef & vegetable stirfry

250 g dried thin egg noddles
spray of canola or olive oil
500 g premium lean beef, cut into thin strips
2 teaspoons minced ginger
1 teaspoon minced garlic
1 onion, diced
1 packet frozen Asian stirfry vegetables
½ cup plum sauce
2 tablespoons MAGGI Sweet Chilli Sauce
80 mL (⅓ cup) MAGGI Chicken Stock

Cook noodles in a large pan of boiling water for 5 minutes or until tender. Spray a nonstick wok or frying pan with oil and heat. Cook the beef in 2 or 3 batches over a high heat for 2–3 minutes or until browned. Set aside. Reheat the wok, add the ginger, garlic, and the onion and stirfry for 2 minutes. Add the frozen vegetables and cook until tender but still crisp. Add the sauces and stock and bring to the boil. Add the noodles and toss through to warm. Return the beef to the pan and serve.

DAY 2
no-fuss bolognese sauce

500 g spaghetti
spray canola or olive oil
1 kg lean minced beef
2 x 575 g jars pasta sauce (reserve ½ cup for risotto on day 3)
sprinkle of grated reduced-fat cheese

Boil water in a large saucepan and cook the spaghetti until al dente. Meanwhile, spray a wok or large saucepan with oil and heat. Add the mince and cook until browned. Add pasta sauce and stir thoroughly. (To turn the sauce into a complete meal, add a packet of frozen mixed vegetables at this stage.) Serve the bolognese sauce over spaghetti and sprinkle with grated cheese.

HINT: *This recipe makes a 'double' quantity of sauce, leaving half for dinner on day 4.*

DAY 3
chicken & corn risotto

spray canola or olive oil
1 onion, finely chopped
1½ cups arborio rice
400 g chicken breast fillet, cut into strips
425 g can baby corn cuts, drained
1 small red capsicum, chopped
1 cup broccoli florets
1 litre (4 cups) MAGGI Chicken Stock
½ cup tomato-based pasta sauce
2 tablespoons chopped fresh basil and parsley (optional)
freshly ground black pepper, to taste

Spray a large pan with oil and heat. Add the onion, rice, chicken, corn, capsicum and broccoli. Cook, stirring, over medium heat for 2 minutes. Add the stock and pasta sauce and stir until well combined. Bring to the boil, reduce the heat to low and simmer, covered, for 20–25 minutes. Stir frequently until the rice is tender and all the liquid is absorbed. Remove from the heat and stand, covered, for 5 minutes. Stir in herbs and season to taste before serving.

DAY 4
spicy burritos

BURRITO SAUCE
bolognese sauce (from day 2)
440 g can red kidney beans
2 tablespoons MAGGI Chilli Sauce (or to taste)

4 plain tortillas (8 if you're really hungry)
½ head of lettuce, shredded
3 tomatoes, diced
60 g grated reduced-fat cheese
low-fat natural yogurt

Heat a saucepan, add the bolognese sauce and then the beans and chilli sauce. Stir to combine and heat through. To serve: take 1 tortilla, place sauce, lettuce and tomato on it, and then add a sprinkle of cheese and a dollop of natural yogurt. Roll up the tortilla and eat.

Day 5
chicken burgers

spray of canola or olive oil
4 chicken breasts
½ lettuce
2 tomatoes
small can of beetroot
1 carrot, grated
8 crusty bread rolls

Spray a nonstick wok or frying pan with oil and heat, or heat a grill. Cook chicken until lightly browned all over and cooked through. Place lots of salad ingredients in a bread roll with the chicken, and serve.

HINT: *You can also cook these chicken burgers on a barbecue.*

DAY 6
pasta with creamy ham sauce

500 g pasta
spray canola or olive oil
1 onion, chopped
1 teaspoon minced garlic
150 g mushrooms, chopped
200 g lean ham, sliced
1 tablespoon cornflour
525 mL (2 cups) CARNATION Light and Creamy
    Evaporated Milk
pepper, to taste

Boil water in a large saucepan and cook the pasta until al dente. Spray a nonstick frying pan with oil and heat. Lightly cook the onion, garlic, mushrooms and ham. Mix the cornflour with a quarter of the evaporated milk until smooth. Add this and the rest of the milk to the onion mixture and heat until the sauce thickens. Season to taste. Pour the sauce over pasta and serve with a mixed salad.

DAY 7
pizza night

2 large pizza bases (spread with tomato paste)
2 onions, finely sliced
2 handfuls reduced-fat grated cheese
leftover ingredients (tomatoes, capsicum, mushrooms)
1 can pineapple
1 barbecue chicken (roughly chopped)
100 g mushrooms, sliced

Preheat the oven to 180°C (350°F). Add ingredients to pizza bases as desired. This is the last night of your stay, so use up all those leftover ingredients. Remember, almost anything goes on a pizza. Place in the oven and bake for about 15 minutes.

making sense of food labels

Many convenience foods are great as shortcuts or for easy meal preparation, but it can be hard to identify which of the vast array of foods in the supermarket belongs in your shopping trolley. Fortunately, many products provide nutrition information on their labels and these can help to make your decision easier. Nutrition information panels are set out in the following way.

NUTRITION INFORMATION SERVINGS PER PACK: 1 SERVING SIZE: 150 g		
	PER SERVE	PER 100 g
ENERGY	618 kJ	412 kJ
PROTEIN	7.8 g	5.2 g
FAT	0.6 g	0.4 g
CARBOHYDRATE		
- TOTAL	27.3 g	18.2 g
- SUGARS	27.3 g	18.2 g
SODIUM	93 mg	62 mg
CALCIUM	411 mg	274 mg
POTASSIUM	330 mg	220 mg

The panel summarises the content of some important nutrients in a food product. These details are provided per 100 g of the food (which makes it easy to compare with other foods), and per 'serve' (take into account that this serve may be quite different from the amount you usually eat). Use the information to gauge how your anticipated serve of this food will contribute to your nutrition goals. For example, will it help you meet your daily target of 800 mg of calcium? Is this food a good choice to fit within your daily fat budget? How much would you have to eat to get 50 g of carbohydrate?

There are many claims on products which sound enticing but they can be misleading. Watch out for some of the following and understand what they really mean:

- REDUCED-FAT ~ The product contains less fat than the original version (usually 25 per cent less). It is not necessarily low in fat. For example, reduced-fat cheese is still a high-fat food.
- LOW-FAT ~ According to Australian Food Regulations, products may only be labelled low-fat if they contain less than a specified amount of fat. Any product labelled in this way is worth looking at.
- LITE OR LIGHT ~ However it is spelt, this is a claim that requires further investigation. Lite or Light can refer to colour, flavour, salt or fat. Check the nutrition information panel.
- LOW-CHOLESTEROL ~ Low-cholesterol products are not always low in fat. Check the fat content on the nutrition information panel.
- OVEN-BAKED ~ These products may be 'baked not fried' but they can still be very high in fat.
- ALL NATURAL ~ Being natural does not always mean the food is good for you. Fat is natural but not desirable in large quantities. Check the nutrition information panel.
- 90% FAT-FREE ~ Means the product contains 10 per cent fat. It does not mean the food contains 90% less fat.

Unfortunately, it is the less nutritious products on the market that tend not to provide a nutrition information panel, but you can still get a feel for the product by examining the ingredient list. Ingredients are listed in order of quantity, starting with the greatest amounts. As a general guide, foods with a fat source as one of the first 2 or 3 ingredients are usually not great choices and should be eaten in small amounts or less regularly. The following table will help you recognise some of the sources of fat, fibre or carbohydrate and also some of their other names.

FAT	CARBOHYDRATE	FIBRE
Vegetable oil	Glucose	Oats
Copha	Maltose	Cereal
Milk solids	Sucrose	Bran
Palm oil	Glucose syrup	NSP
Shortening	Maltodextrin	Rice
Cocoa butter	Dextrose	
Cream	Juice concentrate	

PERCENTAGE OF FAT

Food manufacturers discuss percentages according to the weight (mass) of the ingredient or nutrient. A food product with 10 per cent fat contains 10 per cent of its mass as fat. However, nutritionists are also interested in the proportion of kilojoules this represents. Ten per cent fat by weight does not mean 10 per cent of energy or kilojoules. After all, fat, protein and carbohydrate provide different energy values, and the water content of a food can distort the kilojoule to mass ratio.

In our recipes, we have stated the energy value of the food, but you can easily calculate the percentage of energy provided by a nutrient in the products you buy using the following method:

- Read the food label to find the quantity (by gram weight) of the nutrient in a serve
- Multiply grams of fat by 37, grams of carbohydrate by 16, and grams of protein by 17
- Divide this number by the kilojoule value of the same portion of the food, multiply by 100, and you have the percentage of energy provided by the nutrient.

glossary & conversions

conversions

Liquid Measures

20 mL	= 1 tablespoon	
60 mL	= 1/4 cup	= 2 fl oz
80 mL	= 1/3 cup	= 2³/4 fl oz
125 mL	= 1/2 cup	= 4 fl oz
250 mL	= 1 cup	= 8 fl oz
1 litre	= 4 cups	= 32 fl oz

Weight Measures

15 g	= 1/2 oz
30 g	= 1 oz
250 g	= 1/2 lb
500 g	= 1 lb

Length Measures

2.5 mm	= 1/8 inch
5 mm	= 1/4 inch
1 cm	= 1/2 inch
2 cm	= 3/4 inch
2.5 cm	= 1 inch

Oven Temperatures

	°C	°F	Gas Mark
Very Slow	120	250	1/2
Slow	150	300	2
Warm (moderately slow)	160	315	3
Moderate	180	350	4
Moderately Hot	190	375	5-6
Hot	210	415	6-7
Very Hot	230	450	8-9

glossary

al dente
The cooked texture of pasta when it's ready to eat. Means just firm to the bite.

baking
To cook by dry heat in an oven.

baste
To spoon hot liquid over food as it cooks.

blanch
Place in boiling water for a short time then plunge into cold water.

crouton
Small square or dice of fried bread or potato. Used to accompany soups and salads.

dice
Cut into small cubes.

garnish
To decorate, improve the appearance of the dish.

ghee
Clarified unsalted butter (of Indian origin).

grilling
To cook using dry heat either under an open grill or on a grill plate.

marinate
To soak raw foods in an aromatic liquid to increase the tenderness and impart flavour.

poach
To cook in water or seasoned liquid in an open pan at simmering point with just enough liquid to cover the food.

puree
To mash and sieve food into a smooth consistency.

sauté
To fry briskly using a small amount of oil in a shallow frying pan over moderately high heat. The food is turned or tossed for even browning.

simmer
To keep a liquid at just below boiling point so that only small bubbles rise to the surface.

steam
To cook by vapour from boiling water.

zest
The coloured, oily outer skins of citrus fruit.

index